COMMON CORE GRADE
ENGLISH 5
WORKBOOK

prepaze

www.prepaze.com

Author: Ace Academic Publishing

Ace Academic Publishing is a leading supplemental educational workbook publisher for grades K-12. At Ace Academic Publishing, we realize the importance of imparting analytical and critical thinking skills during the early ages of childhood and hence our books include materials that require multiple levels of analysis and encourage the students to think outside the box.

The materials for our books are written by award winning teachers with several years of teaching experience. All our books are aligned with the state standards and are widely used by many schools throughout the country.

Prepaze is a sister company of Ace Academic Publishing. Intrigued by the unending possibilities of the internet and its role in education, Prepaze was created to spread the knowledge and learning across all corners of the world through an online platform. We equip ourselves with state-of-the-art technologies so that knowledge reaches the students through the quickest and the most effective channels.

For inquiries and bulk orders, contact Ace Academic Publishing at the following address:

Ace Academic Publishing
3736 Fallon Road #403
Dublin CA 94568

www.aceacademicpublishing.com

Ace Academic Publishing
ACHIEVING EXCELLENCE TOGETHER

ISBN: 978-1-949383-11-9

INTRODUCTION

About the Book

The content of the book includes multiple chapters and units covering all the required Common Core Standards for the grade level. Similar to a standardized exam, you can find questions of all types: Multiple Choice, Fill in the Blanks, True or False, Match the Correct Answer and Explain Your Answers. The carefully chosen reading comprehension passages will help the students gain key comprehension skills, such as recognizing themes and character traits and understanding figurative language and contextual vocabulary. The questions also cover writing standards that are not covered by most of the other commonly available workbooks. The exercises help students learn proper language conventions and effectively use resources to research topics for writing essays. The detailed answer explanations help the students make sense of the problems and gain confidence in solving similar problems.

For the Parents

This workbook includes practice questions and tests that cover all the required Common Core Standards for the grade level. The book comprises multiple tests for each topic area so that your child can retake another test on the same topic. The workbook also includes questions for the writing standards and teaches your child how to write essays and free responses. The workbook is divided into chapters and units so that you can choose the topics that you want your child to practice. The detailed answer explanations will teach your child the right methods to solve the problems for all types of questions, including the free response questions. After completing the tests on all the chapters, your child can take any Common Core standardized exam with confidence.

For additional online practice, sign up for a free account at www.aceacademicprep.com.

For the Teachers

All questions and tests included in the Workbook are based on the State Standards and include a clear label of the standard name. By following the chapter units, you can assign your students tests on a particular topic. The Workbook will help your students overcome any deficiencies in their understanding of critical concepts and will also help you identify specific topics that may require more practice. The grade-appropriate yet challenging questions will help your students learn to strategically use appropriate tools and persevere through Common Core standardized exams.

For additional online practice, sign up for a free account at www.aceacademicprep.com.

Other books from Ace Academic Publishing

    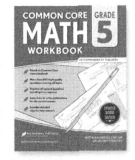

 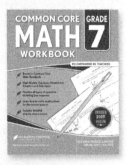 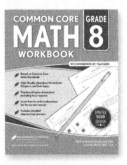  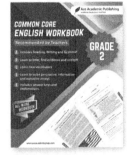

 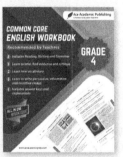  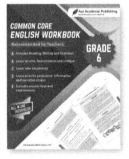 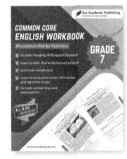

Ace Academic Publishing
ACHIEVING EXCELLENCE TOGETHER

TABLE OF CONTENTS

GRADE 5

1. READING: LITERATURE

1.1. **KEY IDEAS AND DETAILS** **8**
Make Inferences • Central Theme • Characters and Setting

1.2. **CRAFT AND STRUCTURE** **15**
Word Meanings • Poem Elements and Structure •
Describe a Narrator's Point of View

1.3. **INTEGRATION OF KNOWLEDGE AND IDEAS** **26**
Analyze Visual and Multimedia Elements •
Compare and Contrast Stories in the Same Genre

1.4. **CHAPTER REVIEW** **49**

2. READING: INFORMATIONAL TEXT

2.1. **KEY IDEAS AND DETAILS** **68**
Quote Accurately from a Text • Determine Main Ideas and
Key Details • Explain Relationships

2.2. **CRAFT AND STRUCTURE** **75**
Word Meanings • Text Structure • Analyze Differences in Point of View

2.3. **INTEGRATION OF KNOWLEDGE AND IDEAS** **83**
Demonstrate the Ability to Locate an Answer to a Question Quickly •
Supporting Evidence • Integrate Information from Several Texts

2.4. **CHAPTER REVIEW** **92**

3. READING: FOUNDATIONAL SKILLS

3.1. **PHONICS AND WORD RECOGNITION** **104**
Letter-sound Correspondences and Syllabication Patterns •
Prose and Poetry • Read with Accuracy to Support Comprehension

3.2. **CHAPTER REVIEW** **110**

4. WRITING

4.1. **TEXT TYPES AND PURPOSES** **118**
Opinion Pieces • Informative/Explanatory Writing • Narrative Writing

4.2. **PRODUCTION AND DISTRIBUTION OF WRITING** **126**
Clarity and Coherency in Writing • Develop and Strengthen Writing

4.3. **RESEARCH TO BUILD AND PRESENT KNOWLEDGE** **133**
Build Knowledge Through Investigation • Summarize or Paraphrase
Information • Draw Evidence from Literary or Informational Texts

4.4. **CHAPTER REVIEW** **142**

5. LANGUAGE

5.1. CONVENTIONS OF STANDARD ENGLISH 154
Grammar and Usage • Conjunctions, Prepositions, and Interjections •
Perfect Verb Tenses • Capitalization, Punctuation, and Spelling

5.2. KNOWLEDGE OF LANGUAGE 159
Expand, Combine, and Reduce Sentences • Compare and
Contrast the Varieties of English (e.g. dialects, registers)

5.3. VOCABULARY ACQUISITION AND USE 166
Word Meanings • Word Origins • Reference Materials •
Figurative Language

5.4. CHAPTER REVIEW 173

END OF YEAR ASSESSMENT 182

ANSWER KEY 207

1. READING: LITERATURE

1.1. KEY IDEAS AND DETAILS   **8**
   ❖ Make Inferences
   ❖ Central Theme
   ❖ Characters and Setting

2.2. CRAFT AND STRUCTURE   **15**
   ❖ Word Meanings
   ❖ Poem Elements and Structure
   ❖ Describe a Narrator's Point of View

3.3. INTEGRATION OF KNOWLEDGE AND IDEAS   **26**
   ❖ Analyze Visual and Multimedia Elements
   ❖ Compare and Contrast Stories in the Same Genre

4.4. CHAPTER REVIEW   **49**

1. READING: LITERATURE

~~ 1.1. Key Ideas and Details ~~

Common Core State Standards: CCSS.ELA-LITERACY.RL.5.1, CCSS.ELA-LITERACY.RL.5.2, CCSS.ELA-LITERACY.RL.5.3

Skills:

- Quote accurately from a text when explaining what the text says explicitly and when drawing inferences from the text.
- Determine a theme of a story, drama, or poem from details in the text; summarize the text.
- Compare and contrast two or more characters, settings, or events in a story or drama, drawing on specific details.

> ➢ **Directions:** *Read the passage and answer the questions below. Choose the best possible answer.*

NOISE IN THE ATTIC

One night, David was suddenly startled while sleeping. He woke up to the faint sound of a mouse scurrying overhead in the attic. His first reaction was to try to go back to sleep. It was midnight and he had to wake up in five hours for work. However, the sound of the mouse running across the wooden floors of the attic became so distracting that he wasn't able to go back to sleep. David realized that if he wanted to get any more sleep, he had to try to stop the noise.

He decided to build a mousetrap in order to catch the mouse. He went outside to the barn and gathered the tools he would need to construct the trap. After assembling it, he placed a slice of cheese on one end so that the mouse would be tempted to go near the trap. David hid in a dark corner of the attic and waited to see if his plan would work.

After patiently waiting for 15 minutes, David heard a loud snap. He quickly shifted over toward the mousetrap.

"Yes! I caught the mouse!" David exclaimed.

He carefully grabbed the trap and went back outside with it. As soon as he was at a safe distance from the house, David opened the trap and set the mouse free.

prepaze   **www.prepaze.com**

1. READING: LITERATURE

═══════ **MULTIPLE CHOICE** ═══════

1. **Which line best describes why David was startled?** (RL.5.1)

   A. "One night, David was suddenly startled while sleeping."

   B. "He woke up to the faint sound of a mouse scurrying overhead in the attic."

   C. "His first reaction was to try to go back to sleep."

   D. "However, the sound of the mouse running across the wooden floors of the attic became so distracting that he wasn't able to go back to sleep."

2. **What can you infer about David?** (RL.5.1)

   A. David is scared of mice.   **B.** David lives alone.
   C. David needs his sleep.   **D.** David is a farmer.

3. **What is the theme of the story's introduction?** (RL.5.2)

   A. Friendship with all   **B.** Man against nature
   C. A quest for discovery   **D.** Technology in society

 prepaze

1. READING: LITERATURE

4. How is the event in the introduction different from the event in the conclusion? (RL.5.3)

A. A mouse is running around David's attic
B. David has to build a mousetrap
C. David has to sleep to be ready for work in five hours
D. David's neighbor is banging on his door

5. What does the passage not explain? (RL.5.1)

A. How David constructed the trap
B. Why David had to get enough sleep
C. Where the noise was coming from
D. What the mouse looked like

6. Which quote best describes what the mousetrap looked like? (RL.5.1)

A. "He decided to build a mouse trap in order to catch the mouse."
B. "He went outside to the barn and gathered the tools he would need to construct the trap."
C. "After assembling it, he placed a slice of cheese on one end so that the mouse would be tempted to go near the trap."
D. "David hid in a dark corner of the attic and waited to see if his plan would work."

7. What challenge did David overcome in the passage? (RL.5.2)

A. David was able to find the tools to build a mousetrap
B. David was able to solve his problem of not being able to sleep
C. David was able to fall back asleep
D. David was able to get to work on time the next day

8. How does David compare to the mouse? (RL.5.3)

A. David and the mouse are both sleeping
B. David and the mouse are both stuck in the barn
C. David and the mouse are both in the attic for at least 15 minutes
D. David and the mouse both got hurt in the mousetrap

1. READING: LITERATURE

9. **How would you summarize the passage?** (RL.5.2)
   A. David is woken up by a mouse in the attic
   B. A mouse gets stuck in a mousetrap in an attic
   C. David catches a mouse in the attic with a mousetrap so he can go back to sleep
   D. David builds a mousetrap with tools he finds in the barn

10. **What can you infer about the mouse from the passage?** (RL.5.1)
    A. The mouse is trying to find its way out of the attic
    B. The mouse is David's pet that got out of its cage
    C. The mouse came from the barn
    D. The mouse had been in the house for a few days

> **Directions:** *Read the passage and answer the questions below. Choose the best possible answer.*

SUNDAY MORNING BREAKFAST

1 It was a weekly tradition in Emma's household for her mom to cook a hearty Sunday morning breakfast. Emma loved waking up to the pleasant smell of warm breakfast food drifting upstairs to her bedroom.

2 On one particular Sunday morning, Emma's mom woke up with the flu. Emma was crushed. She knew her dad and brothers looked forward to the tradition as much as she did. After pondering what she should do for a few minutes, she eventually decided that she would try to cook the family breakfast on her own.

...continued next page

Copyrighted Material prepaze

1.1. KEY IDEAS AND DETAILS

1. READING: LITERATURE

3 Emma began by glancing through a few of her mom's cookbooks and recipes that were stored in the food pantry. She wanted to get an idea of what would be easy for her to make. She settled on French toast, scrambled eggs, and hash browns.

4 Before she started cooking, Emma opened up the refrigerator to check that she had all the ingredients she would need. After scanning the shelves, she quickly realized that there were no eggs left. Emma would need to rethink her breakfast menu. Instead of cooking scrambled eggs and French toast, Emma decided to fry crispy bacon and heat up bagels to go along with the side of hash browns.

1.1. KEY IDEAS AND DETAILS

11. **What can you infer about Emma from the passage?** (RL.5.1)
    A. Emma was a poor cook
    B. Emma was set on keeping her family's tradition
    C. Emma was allergic to bread
    D. Emma was an only child

12. **What is the main theme of the passage?** (RL.5.2)
    A. Admit defeat
    C. Try your best
    B. Be honest
    D. Explore the world

13. **Which line best describes why Emma could not cook French toast and scrambled eggs?** (RL.5.1)
    A. "She settled on French toast, scrambled eggs, and hash browns."
    B. "Before she started cooking, Emma opened up the refrigerator to check that she had all the ingredients she would need."
    C. "After scanning the shelves, she quickly realized that there were no eggs left."
    D. "Emma would need to rethink her breakfast menu."

1. READING: LITERATURE

14. How do Emma and her mom contrast with her brothers and dad? (RL.5.3)

    A. Emma and her mom make Sunday morning breakfast and her dad and brothers do not

    B. Emma and her mom wake up before her dad and brothers on Sunday morning

    C. Emma and her mom go grocery shopping for breakfast items while her dad and brothers stay home

    D. Emma and her mom look forward to eating Sunday breakfast more than her dad and brothers do

15. What can you infer about Emma's family from the passage? (RL.5.1)

    A. Emma has a small family

    B. Traditions are important to Emma's family

    C. Emma's family likes to eat hearty food

    D. Emma's family gets sick quite often

16. How would you summarize the passage? (RL.5.2)

    A. Emma is upset that she has to cook the family breakfast

    B. Emma is nervous because she doesn't know how to cook

    C. Emma makes breakfast for her family after her mom gets sick, to keep the family tradition of eating Sunday breakfast together

    D. Emma has to learn to substitute ingredients when she discovers there are no more eggs to cook French toast

17. What challenge did Emma overcome in the passage? (RL.5.2)

    A. Emma nursed her mom back to health when she fell sick with the flu

    B. Emma cooked Sunday breakfast by herself without the help of her mom

    C. Emma fried bacon instead of making scrambled eggs

    D. Emma had to teach herself how to cook

1.1. KEY IDEAS AND DETAILS

1. READING: LITERATURE

18. **Which paragraph best describes how Emma brainstormed a solution when her mother could not help her make breakfast?** (RL.5.1)

A. Paragraph 1   **B.** Paragraph 2   **C.** Paragraph 3   **D.** Paragraph 4

19. **How does the main event happening in paragraph 2 contrast with the main event happening in paragraph 4?** (RL.5.3)

A. In paragraph 2, Emma learns she has to cook by herself, and in paragraph 4, she accomplishes the task of making breakfast for her family

B. In paragraph 2, Emma's mom is sick, and in paragraph 4, her mom feels better and is able to join the family for breakfast

C. In paragraph 2, Emma's brothers are teasing her about having to cook by herself, and in paragraph 4, her brothers are thankful that she cooked breakfast for them

D. In paragraph 2, Emma doesn't know how to cook, and in paragraph 4, she has taught herself the basics of cooking breakfast

20. **What does the passage not explain?** (RL.5.1)

A. Why Emma's brother and dad don't offer to help her cook

B. Why Emma has to change the breakfast menu

C. Why Emma has to cook breakfast by herself

D. Why Emma wants to cook breakfast without her mom's help

1.2. CRAFT AND STRUCTURE

1. READING: LITERATURE

~~~~ 1.2. Craft and Structure ~~~~

Common Core State Standards: CCSS.ELA-LITERACY.RL.5.4, CCSS.ELA-LITERACY.RL.5.5, CCSS.ELA-LITERACY.RL.5.6

Skills:

- Determine the meaning of words and phrases as they are used in a text.
- Explain how a series of chapters, scenes, or stanzas fits together to provide the overall structure of a particular story, drama, or poem.
- Describe how a narrator's or speaker's point of view influences how events are described.

> ➤ **Directions:** *Read the passage and answer the questions.*

GRIMMS' FAIRY TALES

There was once a forester who went into the forest to hunt. As he entered the forest, he heard what sounded like a little child's scream. He followed the sound and at last came to a high tree. At the top of the tree sat a little child. The mother had fallen asleep under the tree with the child, and a bird of prey had seen it in her arms, flown down, snatched it away, and set it on the high tree.

The forester climbed up, brought the child down, and thought to himself:

"You will take him home with you, and bring him up with your Lina." So he took it home, and the two children grew up together. The one which he had found in the tree was called Fundevogel, because a bird had carried it away. Fundevogel and Lina loved each other so dearly that when they did not see each other they were sad.

...continued next page

   prepaze

1. READING: LITERATURE

Now, the forester had an old cook, who one evening took two pails and began to fetch water, and did not go once only, but many times, out to the spring. Lina saw this and said, "Listen, old Sanna, why are you fetching so much water?"

"If you will never repeat it to anyone, I will tell you why." So Lina said, no, she would never repeat it to anyone, and then the cook said: "Early tomorrow morning, when the forester is out hunting, I will heat the water, and when it is boiling in the kettle, I will throw in Fundevogel and will boil him in it."

=== **TRUE OR FALSE** ===

1. **The angry viewpoint of the cook is shown through her plan towards Fundevogel.** (RL5.6)

   A. True   **B.** False

2. **When the forester would "bring him up," this refers to the path that the forester would take to get the child to his home.** (RL5.4)

   A. True   **B.** False

=== **MULTIPLE CHOICE** ===

3. **Even though the forester kidnapped the child (Fundevogel), the narrator shows a positive viewpoint towards the forester. How does the narrator do this in the story?** (RL5.6)

   A. The forester wants his child to have a playmate
   B. The old cook wants to boil the child
   C. The forester treated the child in a loving way
   D. The author likes forests and shows that he appreciates nature

4. **In what way do you think the last paragraph fits into the overall story?** (RL5.5)

   A. It establishes a problem
   B. It explains the character of the old cook
   C. It shows the interaction between the characters
   D. It solves the problem that the old cook has with the new child

1.2. CRAFT AND STRUCTURE

1. READING: LITERATURE

> **Directions:** *Read the passage and answer the questions.*

GRIMMS' FAIRY TALES

Early the next morning, the forester got up and went out hunting. While he was gone, the children remained in bed. Then Lina said to Fundevogel: "If you will never leave me, I too will never leave you."

Fundevogel said: "Neither now, nor ever will I leave you."

Then," said Lina, "Then will I tell you. Last night, old Sanna carried so many buckets of water into the house that I asked her why she was doing that, and she said that early this morning when father is out hunting, she will set the kettle full of water, throw you into it and boil you; but we will get up quickly, dress ourselves, and go away together."

The two children therefore got up, dressed themselves quickly, and went away. When the water in the kettle was boiling, the old cook went into the bedroom to fetch Fundevogel and throw him into it. But when she came in and went to the beds, both the children were gone. She was terribly alarmed, and said to herself: "What shall I say when the forester comes home and sees that the children are gone? They must be followed instantly to get them back again."

1.2. CRAFT AND STRUCTURE

=== **MULTIPLE CHOICE** ===

5. **What does "fetch" mean, as it was written in the fourth paragraph?** (RL5.4)

   A. To ask a question
   C. To move something
   B. To bring back
   D. To be sold

6. **What does the narrator's description of Lina reveal about her character?** (RL5.6)

   A. She can't keep a secret very well
   B. She is spoiled and wants her friend
   C. She is scared of Fundevogel
   D. She cares for Fundevogel

prepaze

1. READING: LITERATURE

=== FILL IN THE BLANK ===

7. The monologue at the end of the fourth paragraph
    (when the old cook talks to herself) was included in order to
    _____. (RL5.5)

8. The narrator's viewpoint of fear towards Old Sanna is revealed
    through _____.(RL5.6)

> **Directions:**Read the passage and answer the questions.

1.2. CRAFT AND STRUCTURE

GRIMMS' FAIRY TALES

Then the old cook sent three servants after the children, who were to run after and overtake the children. The children, however, were sitting outside the forest, and when they saw the three servants running from afar, Lina said to Fundevogel: "Never leave me, and I will never leave you."

Fundevogel said: "Neither now, nor ever."

Then said Lina: "You become a rosebush, and I the rose upon it." When the three servants came to the forest, nothing was there but a rosebush with one rose upon it. The children were nowhere to be found.

Then said they: "There is nothing to be done here." And they went home and told the old cook that they had seen nothing in the forest but a little rosebush with one rose on it.

Then the old cook scolded and said, "You simpletons! You should have cut the rosebush in two, broken off the rose and brought it home with you. Go and do it at once!" They therefore had to go out and look for a second time.

...continued next page

1. READING: LITERATURE

The children, however, saw them coming from a distance. Then Lina said, "Fundevogel, never leave me and I will never leave you."

Fundevogel said, "Neither now, nor ever."

Said Lina, "Then you become a church, and I'll be the chandelier in it." So when the three servants came, nothing was there but a church, with a chandelier in it.

They said therefore to each other: "What can we do here? Let us go home." When they got home, the old cook asked if they had found the children, and they said no, they had found nothing but a church, with a chandelier in it.

And the old cook scolded them and said, "You fools! Why did you not pull the church to pieces, and bring the chandelier home with you?" Then the old cook herself got on her legs and went with the three servants in pursuit of the children. The children, however, saw from afar that the three servants were coming, with the cook waddling after them.

Then said Lina, "Fundevogel, never leave me, and I will never leave you."

Then said Fundevogel, "Neither now, nor ever."

Said Lina, "Be a fishpond, and I will be the duck upon it." The cook, however, came up to them, and when she saw the pond she lay down by it and was about to drink it up. But the duck swam quickly to her, seized her head in its beak and drew her into the water, and there the old witch drowned. Then the children went home together and were heartily delighted, and if they had not died, they are living still.

=== **MULTIPLE CHOICE** ===

9. **For what reason was the children's changing into the rosebush and church included in the story?** (RL5.5)

   A. To make the servants look foolish

   B. To allow the story to have a happy ending

   C. To show that this was a magical story

   D. To allow the children to trick the servants by looking like objects

1. READING: LITERATURE

10. **The narrator's viewpoint of the character of old Sanna, the cook, is revealed through the cook's words to the servants. What does the narrator have the cook do?** (RL5.6)

   A. She insults the servants and forces them to go back to the forest

   B. She speaks directly to the servants

   C. She gives direct instructions to the servants to go back to the forest

   D. She compliments the servants by calling them simpletons

11. **What is the meaning of "overtake the children" when it is stated at the beginning of the text?** (RL5.4)

   A. Speak to them   **B.** Catch them

   C. Run past them   **D.** Push them down

12. **When the old cook "got on her legs," what does this mean?** (RL5.4)

   A. Stood up   **B.** Put her legs on

   C. Put her shoes on   **D.** Stretched her legs

> **Directions:** *Read the passage and answer the questions.*

A BOY AND HIS STOMACH

What's the matter, stummick? Ain't I always been your friend?
Ain't I always been a pardner to you? All my pennies don't I spend
In getting nice things for you? Don't I give you lots of cake?
Say, stummick, what's the matter, why you had to go an' ache?

Why, I loaded you with good things yesterday;
I gave you more corn an' chicken than you'd ever had before;
I gave you fruit an' candy, apple pie an' chocolate cake,
An' last night when I got to bed you had to go an' ache.

...continued next page

    www.prepaze.com

1. READING: LITERATURE

Say, what's the matter with you? Ain't you satisfied at all?
I gave you all you wanted; you was hard jes' like a ball,
An' you couldn't hold another bit of pudding'; yet last night You
ached most awful, stummick! That ain't treatin' me jest right.

I've been a friend to you, I have! Why ain't you a friend o'
mine? They gave me castor oil becoz you made me whine.
I'm feelin' fine this mornin'; yes it's true;
But I tell you, stummick, you better appreciate the things I do for you.

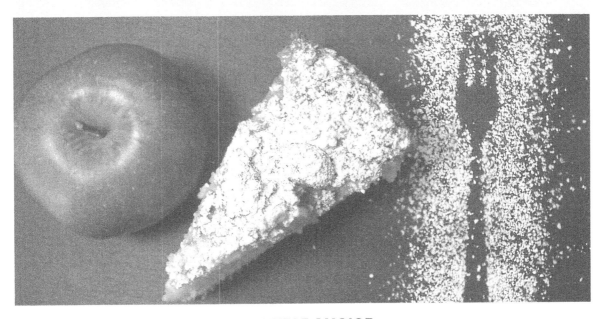

=== **MULTIPLE CHOICE** ===

13. **One stanza mentions different foods the boy eats. Why is this included in the poem?** (RL5.5)

   A. To show that the boy takes care of his stomach

   B. To show that the boy eats proper food

   C. To let the reader know what bad foods the boy eats

   D. To use sensory details in the poem

1. READING: LITERATURE

14. **Why did the author include the last stanza of the poem?** (RL5.5)
    A. To show that the boy does not really understand how he got his stomach issues
    B. To explain that the boy appreciates medicine that cures his stomach issues
    C. To explain that the boy always feels good no matter what he eats
    D. To show the boy's appreciation for his stomach

=== **FREE FORM RESPONSE** ===

15. **What is the narrator's viewpoint of the stomach, based on his descriptions of the stomach's actions in the poem?** (RL5.6)

_____

_____

_____

_____

_____

_____

_____

_____

_____

_____

_____

_____

1.2. CRAFT AND STRUCTURE

1. READING: LITERATURE

16. **What does the author mean when he states, "I loaded you with good things?"** (RL5.4)

_____

_____

_____

_____

_____

_____

_____

_____

_____

_____

1.2. CRAFT AND STRUCTURE

➢ **Directions:** _Read the passage and answer the questions._

FIFTY FAMOUS PEOPLE

One morning, there was a loud knock at Dean Swift's door. His servant opened it. The man who outside handed her a fine duck that had lately been killed, and said, "Here's a present for the Dean. It's from Mr. Boyle."

Then, without another word, he turned and walked away.

...continued next page

 prepaze

1. READING: LITERATURE

A few days afterward, the man came again. This time he brought a partridge. "Here's another bird from Mr. Boyle," he said.

Now, Mr. Boyle was a sporting neighbor who spent a good deal of time shooting. He was a great admirer of Dean Swift and took pleasure in sending him presents of game.

The third time, the man brought a quail. "Here's something else for the Dean," he said roughly, and tossed it into the servant's arms.

=== **MULTIPLE CHOICE** ===

17. **For what reason was the following line included in the text?** (RL5.5)

"Then, without another word, he turned and walked away."

    A. To demonstrate how the man at the door interacts with others
    B. To show the man at the door's nonverbal actions
    C. To reveal the man at the door's cruelty
    D. To point out that the man at the door doesn't like to talk

18. **What is the narrator's viewpoint of the man at the door, based on the way he acts in front of Mr. Swift's servant?** (RL5.6)

    A. the man is calm
    B. the man is appreciative
    C. the man is rude
    D. the man is helpful

19. **Why was the following line included in the text? "...he said roughly, and tossed it into the servant's arms."** (RL5.5)

    A. to explain how the man left the porch in an unusual way
    B. to show the different animals that the man brought to Mr. Swift
    C. to show that the man is getting kinder after each visit
    D. to show that the man's rudeness has increased

1.2. CRAFT AND STRUCTURE

prepaze

www.prepaze.com

1. READING: LITERATURE

20. What does the term "partridge" refer to in the text?(RL5.4)

A. A sport   **B.** A bird   **C.** A neighbor   **D.** A weapon

1.3. INTEGRATION OF KNOWLEDGE AND IDEAS

1. READING: LITERATURE

~~ 1.3. Integration of Knowledge and Ideas ~~

Common Core State Standards: CCSS.ELA-LITERACY.RL.5.7, CCSS.ELA-LITERACY.RL.5.9

Skills:

- Analyze how visual and multimedia elements contribute to the meaning, tone, or beauty of a text.
- Compare and contrast stories in the same genre on their approaches to similar themes and topics.

> **Directions:** *Read the passage below. Answer the questions that follow.*

PETER COTTONTAIL

Once upon a time there were four little rabbits, and their names were Flopsy, Mopsy, Cottontail, and Peter. They lived with their Mother in a sandbank, underneath the root of a very big fir tree. "Now, my dears," said old Mrs. Rabbit one morning, "you may go into the fields or down the lane, but don't go into Mr. McGregor's garden: your father had an accident there; he was put in a pie by Mrs. McGregor. "Now run along, and don't get into mischief. I am going out."

Then old Mrs. Rabbit took a basket and her umbrella to the baker's. She bought a loaf of brown bread and five currant buns. Flopsy, Mopsy, and Cottontail, who were good little bunnies, went down the lane to gather blackberries, but Peter, who was very naughty, ran to Mr. McGregor's garden and squeezed under the gate!

First he ate some lettuces and some French beans; and then he ate some radishes; and then, feeling rather sick, he went to look for some parsley. But round the end of a cucumber frame, whom should he meet but Mr. McGregor!

Mr. McGregor was on his hands and knees planting young cabbages, but he jumped up and ran after Peter, waving a rake and calling out, "Stop thief!" Peter was most dreadfully frightened, for he had forgotten the way back to the gate. He rushed all over the garden, and lost one of his shoes among the cabbages, and the other shoe amongst the potatoes.

...continued next page

1. READING: LITERATURE

After losing them, he ran on four legs and went faster, so that I think he might have got away altogether if he had not unfortunately run into a gooseberry net and got caught by the large buttons on his jacket. It was a blue jacket with brass buttons, quite new.

Peter gave himself up for lost and shed big tears; but his sobs were overheard by some friendly sparrows, who flew to him in great excitement, and implored him to exert himself. Mr. McGregor came up with a sieve, which he intended to pop upon the top of Peter; but Peter wriggled out just in time, leaving his jacket behind him. He rushed into the tool shed and jumped into a can. It would have been a beautiful thing to hide in if it had not had quite so much water in it.

Mr. McGregor was quite sure that Peter was somewhere in the tool shed, perhaps hidden underneath a flowerpot. He began to turn the pots over carefully, looking under each. Presently, Peter sneezed— "Kertyschoo!" Mr. McGregor was after him in no time, and tried to put his foot upon Peter, who jumped out of a window, upsetting three plants. The window was too small for Mr. McGregor, and he was tired of running after Peter. He went back to his work.

═══════ **MULTIPLE CHOICE** ═══════

1. **The following image best illustrates which line from the story?** (RL. 5.7)

   A. "They lived with their Mother in a sand-bank, underneath the root of a very big fir tree."

   B. "Mr. McGregor was after him in no time, and tried to put his foot upon Peter, who jumped out of a window, upsetting three plants."

   C. "First, he ate some lettuces and some French beans; and then he ate some radishes; and then, feeling rather sick, he went to look for some parsley."

   D. "But Peter, who was very naughty, ran to Mr. McGregor's garden and squeezed under the gate!"

1. 3. INTEGRATION OF KNOWLEDGE AND IDEAS

     prepaze

1. READING: LITERATURE

2.   Which picture best illustrates the following line from the story? (RL. 5.7)

"After losing them, he ran on four legs and went faster, so that I think he might have got away altogether if he had not unfortunately run into a gooseberry net and got caught by the large buttons on his jacket. It was a blue jacket with brass buttons, quite new."

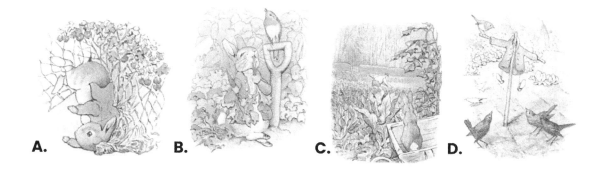

A.   B.   C.   D.

3.   Which of the following images is NOT an accurate illustration of Peter Cottontail? (RL. 5.7)

A.   B.   C.   D.

1. READING: LITERATURE

> **Directions:** *Read the passage below. Answer the questions that follow.*

THE LITTLE OLD WOMAN WHO LIVED IN A SHOE

Once upon a time, there was a Little Old Woman who lived in a shoe. This shoe stood near a great forest, and was so large that it served as a house for the Old Woman and all her children, of which she had so many that she did not know what to do with them.

But the Little Old Woman was very fond of her children, and they only thought of the best way to please her. Strong-arm, the eldest, cut down trees for firewood. Peter made baskets of wickerwork. Mark was the chief gardener. Lizzie milked the cow, and Jenny taught the younger children to read.

Now, this Little Old Woman had not always lived in a shoe. She and her family had once dwelt in a nice house covered with ivy, and her husband had been a woodcutter, like Strong-arm. But a fierce giant lived in a huge castle beyond the forest, who one day came and laid their house in ruins with his club; after which he carried off the poor woodcutter to his castle beyond the forest. When the Little Old Woman came home, her house was in ruins and her husband was nowhere to be seen.

Night came on, and as the father did not return, the Old Woman and her family went to search for him. When they came to the part of the wood where the giant had met their father, they saw an immense shoe. They spent a long time weeping and calling out for their father, but met with no reply. Then the Old Lady thought that they had better take shelter in the shoe until they could build a new house. So Peter and

...continued next page

prepaze

1. READING: LITERATURE

Strong-arm put a roof to it, and cut a door, and turned it into a dwelling. Here they all lived happily for many years, but the Little Old Lady never forgot her husband and his sad fate.

Strong-arm, who saw how wretched his mother often was about it, proposed to the next eleven brothers that they should go with him and set their father free from the giant. Their mother knew the giant's strength, and would not hear of the attempt, as she feared they would be killed. But Strong-arm was not afraid. He bought a dozen sharp swords, and Peter made as many strong shields and helmets, as well as crossbows and iron-headed arrows. They were now quite ready; Strong-arm gave the order to march, and they started for the forest.

The next day they came in sight of the giant's castle. Strong-arm, leaving his brothers in a wood close by, strode boldly up to the entrance and seized the knocker. The door was opened by a funny little boy with a large head, who kept grinning and laughing.

Strong-arm then walked boldly across the courtyard, and presently met a page, who took off his hat and asked him what he wanted. Strong-arm said he had come to liberate his father, who was kept a prisoner by the giant; on this, the little man said he was sorry for him, because the part of the castle in which his father was kept was guarded by a large dragon.

Strong-arm, undaunted, soon found the dragon, who was fast asleep. So Strong-arm made short work of it by sending his sword right through its heart; at which it jumped up, uttering a loud scream, and made as if it would spring forward and seize Strong-arm! But the good sword had done its work, and the monster fell heavily on the ground, dead.

Now the giant was fast asleep in a remote part of the castle. Strong-arm had no sooner finished the dragon, then up started the funny little boy who had opened the door. He led Strong-arm round to another part of the courtyard, where he saw his poor father, who at once sprung to his feet, and embraced him. Then Strong-arm called up his brothers, and when they had embraced their father, they soon broke his chain and set him free.

1. READING: LITERATURE

4. **The following image shows which two characters from the passage?** (RL. 5.7)

  A. The Little Old Woman and her husband
  B. The giant and the dragon
  C. Strong-arm and the funny little boy
  D. Strong-arm and the giant

1.3. INTEGRATION OF KNOWLEDGE AND IDEAS

5. **The following picture best illustrates which sentence from the passage?** (RL. 5.7)

  A. "They spent a long time weeping and calling out for their father, but met with no reply."
  B. "Their mother knew the giant's strength, and would not hear of the attempt, as she feared they would be killed."
  C. "But a fierce giant lived in a huge castle beyond the forest, who one day came and laid their house in ruins with his club; after which he carried off the poor woodcutter to his castle beyond the forest."
  D. "Strong-arm, the eldest, cut down trees for firewood."

1. READING: LITERATURE

> ➢ **Directions:** *Read the paired passages. Then answer the questions that follow.*

SNOW WHITE

There was once a queen who had no children, and it grieved her sorely. One winter's afternoon, she was sitting by the window sewing when she pricked her finger, and three drops of blood fell on the snow. Then she thought to herself: "Ah, what would I give to have a daughter with skin as white as snow and cheeks as red as blood."

After a while, a little daughter came to her with skin as white as snow and cheeks as red as blood. So they called her Snow White.

But before Snow White had grown up, her mother, the Queen, died, and her father married again, to a most beautiful princess who was very vain of her beauty. She was also jealous of all women who might be thought as beautiful as she was. And every morning she used to stand before her mirror and say:

"Mirror, mirror, on the wall,

Who is the fairest of us all?"

And the mirror always used to reply:

"Queen, Queen, on thy throne,

The greatest beauty is thine own."

But Snow White grew fairer and fairer every year, till at last one day when the Queen in the morning spoke to her mirror and said:

"Mirror, mirror, on the wall,

Who is the fairest of us all?"

The mirror replied:

"Queen, Queen, on thy throne,

Snow White's the fairest thou must own."

Then the Queen grew terribly jealous of Snow White, and thought and thought how she could get rid of her. At last, the Queen went to a hunter and engaged him for a large sum of money to take Snow White out into the forest, kill her, and bring back her heart.

...continued next page

1. READING: LITERATURE

CINDERELLA

Once there was a gentleman who married, for his second wife, the proudest and most haughty woman that was ever seen. She had, by a former husband, two daughters of her own humor, who were, indeed, exactly like her in all things. He had likewise, by another wife, a young daughter, but of unparalleled goodness and sweetness of temper, which she took from her mother, who was the best creature in the world.

No sooner were the ceremonies of the wedding over but the mother-in-law began to show herself in her true colors. She could not bear the good qualities of this pretty girl, and the less because they made her own daughters appear the more odious. She employed the girl in the meanest work of the house: she scoured the dishes, tables, etc., and scrubbed madam's chamber, and those of misses, her daughters; she lay up in a sorry garret, upon a wretched straw bed, while her sisters lay in fine rooms, with floors all inlaid, upon beds of the very newest fashion, and where they had looking glasses so large that they might see themselves at their full length from head to foot.

The poor girl bore all patiently, and dared not tell her father, who would have rattled her off; for his wife governed him entirely. When she had done her work, she used to go into the chimney-corner, and sit down among cinders and ashes, which made her commonly be called Cinderwench; but the youngest, who was not so rude and uncivil as the eldest, called her Cinderella. However, Cinderella, notwithstanding her mean apparel, was a hundred times more handsome than her sisters, though they were always dressed very richly.

It happened that the king's son gave a ball, and invited all persons of fashion to it. Our young misses were also invited, for they cut a very grand figure among the quality. They were mightily delighted at this invitation, and wonderfully busy in choosing out such gowns, petticoats, and head-clothes as might become them. This was a new trouble for Cinderella; for it was she who ironed her sisters' linen, and plaited their ruffles; they talked all day long of nothing but how they should be dressed.

"For my part," said the eldest, "I will wear my red velvet suit with French trimming."

...continued next page

Copyrighted Material prepaze

1.3. INTEGRATION OF KNOWLEDGE AND IDEAS

1. READING: LITERATURE

"And I," said the youngest, "shall have my usual petticoat; but then, to make amends for that, I will put on my gold-flowered manteau, and my diamond stomacher, which is far from being the most ordinary one in the world."

They sent for the best tire-woman they could get to make up their head-dresses and adjust their double pinners, and they had their red brushes and patches from Mademoiselle de la Poche. Cinderella was likewise called up to them to be consulted in all these matters, for she had excellent notions, and advised them always for the best, and offered her services to dress their heads, which they were very willing she should do. As she was doing this, they said to her:

"Cinderella, would you not be glad to go to the ball?"

"Alas!" said she, "you only jeer me; it is not for such as I am to go thither."

"Thou art in the right of it," replied they; "it would make the people laugh to see a Cinderwench at a ball."

Anyone but Cinderella would have dressed their heads awry, but she was very good, and dressed them perfectly well They were almost two days without eating, so much were they transported with joy. They broke above a dozen laces in trying to be laced up close, that they might have a fine slender shape, and they were continually at their looking-glass. At last the happy day came; they went to Court, and Cinderella followed them with her eyes as long as she could, and when she had lost sight of them, she fell a-crying.

Her godmother, who saw her all in tears, asked her what was the matter.

"I wish I could--I wish I could--"; she was not able to speak the rest, being interrupted by her tears and sobbing.

This godmother of hers, who was a fairy, said to her, "Thou wishest thou couldst go to the ball; is it not so?"

"Y--es," cried Cinderella, with a great sigh.

"Well," said her godmother, "be but a good girl, and I will contrive that thou shalt go." Then she took her into her chamber, and said to her, "Run into the garden, and bring me a pumpkin."

...continued next page

     www.prepaze.com

1. READING: LITERATURE

Cinderella went immediately to gather the finest she could get, and brought it to her godmother, not being able to imagine how this pumpkin could make her go to the ball. Her godmother scooped out all the inside of it, having left nothing but the rind; which done, she struck it with her wand, and the pumpkin was instantly turned into a fine coach, gilded all over with gold.

MULTIPLE CHOICE

6. **Which is true of the two passages?** (RL. 5.9)

   A. Each passage includes animals who are personified and act as the lead characters

   B. Each passage includes an evil witch and a hero who comes to the rescue of the princess

   C. Each passage includes stepsisters who envy their stepfather's daughter

   D. Each passage includes a girl whose mother has passed away and whose father has remarried

7. **When comparing the two passages, which of the following themes is apparent?** (RL. 5.9)

   A. Inner beauty is as valuable as outer beauty

   B. Jealousy can cause people to do terrible things

   C. Both A and B

   D. Neither A nor B

8. **Which is true of the two passages?** (RL. 5.9)

   A. Both passages are written in the first person point of view

   B. Both passages are written in the third person point of view

   C. The first passage is written in the first person point of view while the second is written in third person point of view

   D. The first passage is written in the third person point of view while the second is written in first person point of view

1.3. INTEGRATION OF KNOWLEDGE AND IDEAS

1. READING: LITERATURE

9. **Which of the following statements concerning the two main characters is true?** (RL. 5.9)

    A. Both Cinderella and Snow White seek ways to get revenge on their stepmothers

    B. Both Cinderella and Snow White seek help from their fathers when they are mistreated by their stepmothers

    C. Both Cinderella and Snow White are patient and compassionate toward their stepmothers even when the stepmothers are mean to them

    D. Both Cinderella and Snow White run away from home because of the way they are treated

10. **Each of the passages has an element of fantasy included. Which option gives evidence to support this statement?** (RL. 5.9)

    A. From Cinderella: "Which done, she struck it with her wand, and the pumpkin was instantly turned into a fine coach, gilded all over with gold. From Snow White: "The mirror replied: "Queen, Queen, on thy throne, Snow White's the fairest thou must own."

    B. From Cinderella: "The poor girl bore all patiently, and dared not tell her father," From Snow White: "There was once a queen who had no children, and it grieved her sorely."

    C. From Cinderella: "As she was doing this, they said to her: 'Cinderella, would you not be glad to go to the ball?'" From Snow White: "But before Snow White had grown up, her mother, the Queen, died."

    D. From Cinderella: "She employed her in the meanest work of the house: she scoured the dishes, tables, etc. From Snow White: "But Snow White grew fairer and fairer every year."

1. READING: LITERATURE

> **Directions:** *Read the passage below. Answer the questions that follow.*

HANSEL AND GRETEL

By a great forest dwelt a poor woodcutter with his wife and his two children. The boy was called Hansel and the girl Gretel. The woodcutter had little to bite and to break, and once, when great dearth fell on the land, he could no longer procure even daily bread.

Now he thought over this by night in his bed and tossed about in his anxiety. He groaned and said to his wife, "What is to become of us? How are we to feed our poor children, when we no longer have anything even for ourselves?"

"I'll tell you what, husband," answered the woman, "early tomorrow morning we will take the children out into the forest to where it is the thickest. There we will light a fire for them and give each of them one more piece of bread, and then we will go to our work and leave them alone. They will not find the way home again, and we shall be rid of them."

"No, wife," said the man, "I will not do that. How can I bear to leave my children alone in the forest? The wild animals would soon come and tear them to pieces."

"Oh! you fool," said she, "then we must all four die of hunger!" And she left him no peace until he consented.

"But I feel very sorry for the poor children, all the same," said the man.

The two children had also not been able to sleep for hunger and had heard what their stepmother had said to their father. Gretel wept bitter tears, and said to Hansel, "Now all is over for us."

"Be quiet, Gretel," said Hansel, "do not distress yourself, I will soon find a way to help us." And when the old folks had fallen asleep, he got up and crept outside. The moon shone brightly, and the white pebbles which lay in front of the house glittered like real silver pennies. Hansel stooped and stuffed the little pocket of his coat with as many as he could get in. Then he went back and said to Gretel, "Be comforted, dear little sister, and sleep in peace. God will not forsake us," and he lay down again in his bed.

...continued next page

1.3. INTEGRATION OF KNOWLEDGE AND IDEAS

prepaze

1. READING: LITERATURE

When day dawned, but before the sun had risen, the woman came and awoke the two children, saying, "Get up, you sluggards. We are going into the forest to fetch wood." She gave each a little piece of bread, and said, "There is something for your dinner, but do not eat it up before then, for you will get nothing else."

When they had walked a short time, Hansel stood still and peeped back at the house, and did so again and again. His father said, "Hansel, what are you looking at there and staying behind for? Pay attention, and do not forget how to use your legs."

"Ah, Father," said Hansel, "I am looking at my little white cat, which is sitting up on the roof, and wants to say goodbye to me." Hansel, however, had not been looking back at the cat, but had been constantly throwing one of the white pebble-stones out of his pocket on the road.

When they had reached the middle of the forest, the father said, "Now, children, pile up some wood, and I will light a fire that you may not be cold." Hansel and Gretel gathered brushwood together, as high as a little hill.

The brushwood was lighted, and when the flames were burning very high, the woman said, "Now, children, lay yourselves down by the fire and rest; we will go into the forest and cut some wood. When we have done, we will come back and fetch you away."

Hansel and Gretel sat by the fire, and when noon came, each ate a little piece of bread. As they had been sitting such a long time, their eyes closed with fatigue, and they fell fast asleep.

When at last they awoke, it was already dark night. Gretel began to cry and said, "How are we to get out of the forest now?"

But Hansel said, "Just wait a little, until the moon has risen, and then we will soon find the way." And when the full moon had risen, Hansel took his little sister by the hand, and followed the pebbles which shone like newly-coined silver pieces and showed them the way.

They walked the whole night long, and by break of day came once more to their father's house. They knocked at the door, and when the woman opened it and saw that it was Hansel and Gretel, she said, "You naughty children, why have you slept so long in the forest? We thought you were never coming back at all."

...continued next page

1. READING: LITERATURE

Not long afterwards, there was once more great dearth throughout the land, and the children heard their step-mother saying at night to their father: "Everything is eaten again, we have one half loaf left, and that is the end. The children must go, we will take them farther into the wood, so that they will not find their way out again. There is no other means of saving ourselves."

The children, however, were still awake and had heard the conversation. When the old folks were asleep, Hansel again got up, and wanted to go out and pick up pebbles as he had done before, but the woman had locked the door, and Hansel could not get out. Nevertheless, he comforted his little sister, and said, "Do not cry, Gretel, go to sleep quietly, the good God will help us."

Early in the morning came the woman and took the children out of their beds. Their piece of bread was still given to them, but it was smaller than before. On the way into the forest, Hansel crumbled his in his pocket, and often stood still and threw a morsel on the ground.

"Hansel, why do you stop and look round?" said the father. "Go on."

"I am looking back at my little pigeon which is sitting on the roof, and wants to say goodbye to me," answered Hansel. Hansel, however, little by little, threw all the crumbs on the path. The woman led the children still deeper into the forest, where they had never in their lives been before.

Then a great fire was again made, and the stepmother said, "Just sit there, you children, and when you are tired you may sleep a little. We are going into the forest to cut wood, and in the evening when we are done, we will come and fetch you away."

When it was noon, Gretel shared her piece of bread with Hansel, who had scattered his by the way. Then they fell asleep. Evening passed, but no one came to help the poor children.

They did not awaken until it was dark. Hansel comforted his little sister and said, "Just wait, Gretel, until the moon rises, and then we shall see the crumbs of bread which I have strewn about. They will show us our way home again." When the moon came they set out, but they found no crumbs, for the many thousands of birds which fly about in the woods and fields, had picked them all up. Hansel said to Gretel, "We shall soon find the way."

...continued next page

1. READING: LITERATURE

But they did not find it. They walked the whole night and all the next day, but they did not get out of the forest, and were very hungry. Soon they were so weary that their legs would carry them no longer, so they lay down beneath a tree and fell asleep.

It was now three mornings since they had left their father's house. They began to walk again, but they always came deeper into the forest. Finally, they reached a little house. They saw that it was built of bread and covered with cakes, but that the windows were of clear sugar.

"We will set to work on that," said Hansel, "and have a good meal. I will eat a bit of the roof, and you, Gretel, can eat some of the window; it will taste sweet."

Hansel reached up above and broke off a little of the roof to try how it tasted, and Gretel leaned against the window and nibbled at the panes. Then a soft voice cried from the parlor - "Nibble, nibble, gnaw, who is nibbling at my little house?"

The children answered, "The wind, the wind, the heaven-born wind," and went on eating without disturbing themselves.

Suddenly the door opened, and a woman as old as the hills, who supported herself on crutches, came creeping out. Hansel and Gretel were so terribly frightened that they let fall what they had in their hands.

═══════════ **MULTIPLE CHOICE** ═══════════

11. The following picture illustrates which sentence from the passage? (RL. 5.7)

A. "Hansel, however, had not been looking back at the cat, but had been constantly throwing one of the white pebble-stones out of his pocket on the road."

B. "Hansel and Gretel gathered brushwood together, as high as a little hill."

C. "And as they had been sitting such a long time, their eyes closed with fatigue, and they fell fast asleep."

D. "But Hansel comforted her and said, "Just wait a little, until the moon has risen, and then we will soon find the way."

 www.prepaze.com

1. READING: LITERATURE

12. Which picture best illustrates what happened to Hansel's breadcrumbs as the children were sleeping? (RL. 5.7)

A.

B.

C.

D.

13. Which of the following pictures DOES NOT belong in this passage? (RL. 5.7)

A.

B.

C.

D.

1.3. INTEGRATION OF KNOWLEDGE AND IDEAS

prepaze

1. READING: LITERATURE

14. **Which sentence in the story is illustrated in the following picture?** (RL. 5.7)

- **A.** "Suddenly the door opened, and a woman as old as the hills, who supported herself on crutches, came creeping out."
- **B.** "We will set to work on that," said Hansel, "and have a good meal."
- **C.** "Then a great fire was again made, and the stepmother said, "Just sit there, you children, and when you are tired you may sleep a little."
- **D.** "Finally, they reached a little house."

15. **If you are creating a Power Point to summarize the story's plot, which of the following should NOT be included?** (RL. 5.7)

- **A.** The appeal of the old woman's home
- **B.** The stepmother's contribution to the plot
- **C.** The woodcutter's care for his tools
- **D.** The children's conflict with the old woman

> **Directions:** *Read the paired passages. Then answer the questions that follow.*

THE LITTLE RED HEN

A Little Red Hen lived in a barnyard. She spent almost all of her time walking about the barnyard in her picketty-pecketty fashion, scratching everywhere for worms.

She dearly loved fat, delicious worms and felt they were absolutely necessary to the health of her children. Every time she found a worm, she would call "Chuck-chuck-chuck!" to her chickies.

...continued next page

1. READING: LITERATURE

When they were gathered about her, she would distribute choice morsels of her tid-bit. A busy little body was she!

A Cat usually napped lazily in the barn door, not even bothering herself to scare the Rat who ran here and there as he pleased. And as for the Pig who lived in the sty – he did not care what happened, so long as he could eat and grow fat.

One day the Little Red Hen found a seed. It was a wheat seed, but the Little Red Hen was so accustomed to bugs and worms that she supposed this to be some new and perhaps very delicious kind of meat. She bit it gently and found that it resembled a worm in no way whatsoever as to taste; although, because it was long and slender, a Little Red Hen might easily be fooled by its appearance.

Carrying it about, she made many inquiries as to what it might be. She found it was a wheat seed and that, if planted, it would grow up, and when ripe it could be made into flour and then into bread.

When she discovered that, she knew it ought to be planted. She was so busy hunting food for herself and her family that, naturally, she thought she ought not to take time to plant it.

She thought of the Pig - upon whom time must hang heavily, and of the Cat who had nothing to do, and of the great fat Rat with his idle hours, and she called loudly: "Who will plant this seed?"

But the Pig said, "Not I," and the Cat said, "Not I," and the Rat said, "Not I."

"Well, then," said the Little Red Hen, "I will." And she did.

She went on with her daily duties through the long summer days, scratching for worms and feeding her chicks, while the Pig grew fat, and the Cat grew fat, and the Rat grew fat, and the wheat grew tall and ready for harvest.

So one day the Little Red Hen chanced to notice how large the wheat was and that the grain was ripe, so she ran about calling briskly: "Who will cut the wheat?"

The Pig said, "Not I," the Cat said, "Not I," and the Rat said, "Not I."

"Well, then," said the Little Red Hen, "I will." And she did.

...continued next page

 prepaze

1. READING: LITERATURE

She got the sickle from among the farmer's tools in the barn and proceeded to cut off all of the big plants of wheat.

On the ground lay the nicely cut wheat, ready to be gathered and threshed, but the newest and yellowest and downiest of Mrs. Hen's chicks set up a "peep-peep-peeping" in its most vigorous fashion, proclaiming to the world at large, but most particularly to its mother, that she was neglecting it.

Poor Little Red Hen! She felt quite bewildered and hardly knew where to turn.

Her attention was sorely divided between her duty to her children and her duty to the wheat, for which she felt responsible.

So, again, in a very hopeful tone, she called out, "Who will thresh the wheat?"

But the Pig, with a grunt, said, "Not I," and the Cat, with a meow, said, "Not I," and the Rat, with a squeak, said, "Not I."

So the Little Red Hen, looking, it must be admitted, rather discouraged, said, "Well, I will, then." And she did.

Of course, she had to feed her babies first, and when she had gotten them all to sleep for their afternoon nap, she went out and threshed the wheat. Then she called out: "Who will carry the Wheat to the mill to be ground?"

Turning their backs with snippy glee, that Pig said, "Not I," and that Cat said, "Not I," and that Rat said, "Not I."

So the good Little Red Hen could do nothing but say, "I will then." And she did.

Carrying the sack of wheat, she trudged off to the distant mill. There she ordered the wheat ground into beautiful white flour. When the miller brought her the flour she walked slowly back all the way to her own barnyard in her own picketty-pecketty fashion.

She even managed, in spite of her load, to catch a nice juicy worm now and then and had one left for the babies when she reached them. Those cunning little fluff-balls were so glad to see their mother. For the first time, they really appreciated her.

After this really strenuous day, Mrs. Hen retired to her slumbers earlier than usual - indeed, before the colors came into the sky to herald the setting of the sun, her usual bedtime hour.

...continued next page

www.prepaze.com

1. READING: LITERATURE

She would have liked to sleep late, but her chicks, joining in the morning chorus of the hen yard, drove away all hope of such a luxury. Even as she sleepily half opened one eye, the thought came to her that today the wheat must somehow, be made into bread.

She was not in the habit of making bread, although, of course, anyone can make it if he or she follows the recipe with care. However, she knew perfectly well that she could do it if necessary.

So after her children were fed and made sweet and fresh for the day, she hunted up the Pig, the Cat and the Rat.

Still confident that they would surely help her someday she sang out, "Who will make the bread?"

Alas for the Little Red Hen! Once more her hopes were dashed! For the Pig said, "Not I," the Cat said, "Not I," and the Rat said, "Not I."

So the Little Red Hen said once more, "I will then," and she did.

Feeling that she might have known all the time that she would have to do it all herself, she went and put on a fresh apron and spotless cook's cap. First of all, she set the dough, as was proper. When it was time she brought out the molding board and the baking tins, molded the bread, divided it into loaves, and put them into the oven to bake. All the while the Cat sat lazily by, giggling and chuckling.

And close at hand the vain Rat powdered his nose and admired himself in a mirror.

In the distance could be heard the drawn out snores of the dozing Pig.

At last the great moment arrived. A delicious odor was wafted upon the autumn breeze. Everywhere the barnyard citizens sniffed the air with delight.

The Red Hen ambled in her picketty-pecketty way toward the source of all this excitement.

Although she appeared to be perfectly calm, in reality, she could only with difficulty restrain an impulse to dance and sing, for had she not done all the work on this wonderful bread? Small wonder that she was the most excited person in the barnyard!

She did not know whether the bread would be fit to eat, but – joy of joys! – when the lovely brown loaves came out of the oven, they were done to perfection.

...continued next page

prepaze

1. READING: LITERATURE

Then, probably because she had acquired the habit, the Red Hen called: "Who will eat the bread?"

All the animals in the barnyard were watching hungrily and smacking their lips in anticipation, and the Pig said, "I will," the Cat said, "I will," the Rat said, "I will."

But the Little Red Hen said, "No, you won't. I will." And she did.

1.3. INTEGRATION OF KNOWLEDGE AND IDEAS

THE ANIMALS' PLEA

Feed me 'til my belly's full.
Please understand me too.
Know that all I'll ever wish,
Is just to be with you.

I love you unconditionally,
Would die for you indeed.
I hope you love me just the same.
This is all we animals need.

Life in thoughts and words and actions,
Is simple, basic, true.
For peace of mind, don't look for more,
Help me as I help you.

Together then, we'll be as one,
Balanced in awesome truth.
Interlinked on circles Gold,
Growing both, to Sage from youth.

1. READING: LITERATURE

=== **MULTIPLE CHOICE** ===

16. **Which is true of the two passages?** (RL. 5.9)
    A. Both passages are written in the first person point of view
    B. Both passages are written in the third person point of view
    C. The first passage is written in the first person point of view, while the second is written in third person point of view
    D. The first passage is written in third person point of view, while the second is written in first person point of view

17. **When comparing the characters in each of the passages, which of the following statements is true?** (RL. 5.9)
    A. The Little Red Hen and the speaker in the second passage both exhibit an eagerness to work and provide for themselves and their families
    B. The Little Red Hen is eager to work to provide for herself and her family while the speaker in the second passage is content to be fed and cared for by her owner
    C. The Little Red Hen is lazy and does not enjoy working while the speaker in the second passage is eager to work and take care of herself and her owner
    D. Both the Little Red Hen and the speaker in the second passage are lazy and content to be cared for by others

18. **Which statement is true about the two passages?** (RL.5.9)
    A. The first passage is a poem and the second is a short story
    B. Both passages are poems
    C. The first passage is a short story and the second is a poem
    D. Both passages are short stories

1.3. INTEGRATION OF KNOWLEDGE AND IDEAS

1. READING: LITERATURE

19. **Personification is when an author gives an animal or object human characteristics and abilities. Which of the following statements is true about the two passages?** (RL. 5.9)

    A. The authors of both passages use personification in their writing

    B. Neither author uses personification in their writing

    C. The author of the first passage uses personification, but the second does not

    D. The author of the second passage uses personification, but the first does not

20. **Dialogue is a conversation between two or more characters, while a monologue is a long speech by only one person. Which of the following statements is true of the two passages?** (RL. 5.9)

    A. The first passage contains dialogue while the second is a monologue

    B. The first passage is a monologue while the second contains dialogue

    C. Both passages are monologues

    D. Both passages contain dialogue

1.4. Chapter Review

1. READING: LITERATURE

~ 1.4. Chapter Review ~

> **Directions:** *Read the passage and answer the questions.*

FIFTY FAMOUS PEOPLE

The servant complained to her master. "That fellow has no manners," she said.

"The next time he comes," said the Dean, "let me know, and I will go to the door." It was not long until the man came with another present. The Dean went to the door.

"Here's a rabbit from Mr. Boyle," said the man.

"See here," said the Dean in a stern voice, "that is not the way to deliver a message. Just step inside and make believe that you are Dean Swift. I will go out and make believe that I am bringing him a present. I will show you how a messenger ought to behave."

"I'll agree to that," said the man; and he stepped inside. The Dean took the rabbit and went out of the house. He walked up the street to the next block. Then he came back and knocked gently at the door.

The door was opened by the man from Mr. Boyle's. The Dean bowed gracefully and said, "If you please, sir, Mr. Boyle's compliments, and he wishes you to accept this fine rabbit."

"Oh, thank you," said the man, very politely. Then taking out his purse, he offered the Dean a shilling. "And here is something for your trouble."

The lesson in manners was not forgotten; for, always after that, the man was very polite when he brought his presents. The Dean also took the hint; for he always remembered to give the man a "tip" for his trouble. Jonathan Swift, often called Dean Swift, was famous as a writer on many subjects. Among other books, he wrote "Gulliver's Travels," which you, perhaps, will read sometime.

1.4. CHAPTER REVIEW

1. READING: LITERATURE

═══════════════════ **TRUE OR FALSE** ═══════════════════

1. **The Dean's way of handling the situation reveals the narrator's negative opinion of him.** (RL5.6)

   A. True   **B.** False

2. **When "the Dean also took the hint," the narrator means that the Dean needed to work on his manners as well.** (RL5.4)

   A. True   **B.** False

═══════════════════ **MULTIPLE CHOICE** ═══════════════════

3. **The last two sentences in the text were added for what reason?** (RL5.5)
   A. To explain that the man is more important than the servant
   B. To identify a famous author
   C. To show that Mr. Swift wrote a book about traveling
   D. To influence the reader to read the book Mr. Swift wrote

4. **Why does the story describe the man coming to the door several times ?** (RL5.5)
   A. To show that his rudeness occurred more than once
   B. To present the man from Mr. Boyle's as a bad person
   C. To show how smart Dean Swift is
   D. To show why the servant complains

> **Directions:** *Read the passage and answer the questions.*

FIFTY FAMOUS PEOPLE

Did you ever hear of King Charles the Twelfth, of Sweden? He lived two hundred years ago, and was famous for his courage in defending his country.

One day he was in the midst of a great battle. The small house in which he had taken shelter was almost between the two armies.

...continued next page

1. READING: LITERATURE

He called to one of his officers and bade him sit down and write a short order for him.

The officer began to write, but just as he finished the first word, a bomb came through the roof of the house and struck the floor close by him. He dropped the pen and sprang to his feet. He was pale with fear. "What is the matter?" asked the king.

"Oh, sir," he answered, "the bomb! The bomb!"

"Yes, I see," said the king. "But what has the bomb to do with what I wish you to write? Sit down, and take your pen. When your country is in danger, you should forget your own safety."

═══════════════ **MULTIPLE CHOICE** ═══════════════

5. **How does the first paragraph relate to the rest of the story?** (RL5.5)
    A. It describes the setting of the story
    B. It depicts the character of King Charles
    C. It relays important events about the bomb in the story
    D. It praises the King of Sweden

6. **Based on the actions of the King, what is the author's viewpoint of the King?** (RL5.6)
    A. Brave   **B.** Stupid   **C.** Misunderstood   **D.** Reliable

7. **Why does the author have the bomb dropped through the roof?** (RL5.5)
    A. To allow the officer to say something to the king
    B. To injure the enemy
    C. To order to cause damage to the roof
    D. To show how risky the situation was

8. **What does the word "bade" mean as it is used in the story?** (RL5.4)
    A. To write on a pad of paper   **B.** To answer a question
    C. To command to do something   **D.** To try to purchase something

1. READING: LITERATURE

> ➤ **Directions:** *Read the passage and answer the questions.*

"A FABLE" FROM POEMS TEACHERS ASK FOR

The mountain and the squirrel
Had a quarrel,
And the former called the latter "Little Prig."
Bun replied,
"You are doubtless very big;
But all sorts of things and weather
Must be taken in together,
To make up a year
And a sphere.
And I think it no disgrace
To occupy my place.
If I'm not so large as you,
You are not so small as I,
And not half as spry.
I'll not deny you make
A very pretty squirrel track;
Talents differ; all is well and wisely put;
If I cannot carry forests on my back,
Neither can you crack a nut."

=== **MULTIPLE CHOICE** ===

9. **How would someone be acting if they were "spry" as it is used in the poem?** (RL5.4)

   A. Angry   **B.** Intelligent   **C.** Patient   **D.** Lively

1. READING: LITERATURE

10. **The mountain calls the squirrel "Little Prig." Why does the author include this?** (RL5.5)

    A. To show that the mountain think the squirrel is insignificant

    B. Because the squirrel resembles a little branch

    C. To explain why the squirrel is lost

    D. Because he or she didn't know what else to say

11. **How does the narrator show that he or she thinks the squirrel is just as skillful as a mountain?** (RL5.6)

    A. By showing how big the squirrel is

    B. By insulting the mountain

    C. By having the squirrel explain what it can do

    D. By explaining what the mountain can do

12. **What is the meaning of "I think it no disgrace to occupy my place," as it is stated in the poem?** (RL5.4)

    A. The mountain and squirrel find it odd communicating with each other

    B. The mountain thinks only large items belong on the Earth

    C. The squirrel is ashamed of its position on the Earth

    D. The squirrel is not embarrassed for being so small

> ➤ **Directions:** *Read the passage and answer the questions below. Choose the best answer.*

MAKING IT TO THE FINISH LINE

Austin grew up in a family that was heavily involved in athletics. His dad had been a track and field superstar in college. In 1996, his dad got invited to compete at the national level at the Olympic Trials in Atlanta, Georgia. The numerous awards his dad won over the years were prominently displayed throughout their house.

Because Austin understood how important sports were to his family, he became a track and field athlete himself. He wanted to compete in the same events his dad had: the long jump, hurdles,

...continued next page

1. READING: LITERATURE

and pole vaulting events. Unfortunately for Austin, he was approximately 4 inches shorter in height than his dad. In all three of his events, height was a major factor. Because of this, it would be much harder for him to win.

Austin knew that he was going to struggle more than his dad did at his age. Still, he was determined to compete at the highest level and make his parents proud of him. Being the best athlete he could become the most important goal in Austin's life. His primary focus was on training to excel at his events in time for the state championship track and field meet.

On the morning of the championship meet, Austin was extremely nervous. As he was stretching on the field during warm-ups, he spotted his family up in the stands, ready to cheer him on to victory. The first event would be the 110-meter hurdle. The announcer called out for all participants to line up at their starting block. The starter pistol went off. Austin had successfully cleared four hurdles when all of a sudden his right foot brushed the top of the fifth hurdle and knocked it, and himself, over.

Austin was so upset. He knew he would not win now. The race was over for him. Still, he got back up and finished the race. His dad ran over to meet him at the finish line. "That's my boy!" he said. "That's what real winners do. They get back up and finish strong. You are a true winner in my book!" Austin smiled. He was relieved and thankful that his dad was proud of him after he gave his best effort.

1. READING: LITERATURE

13. **How would you summarize the passage?** (RL.5.2)

   A. Austin wanted to make his dad proud by joining his track and field team

   B. Austin was nervous about competing in the track and field championship meet

   C. Austin competed in the track and field championships to make his family proud, and when he fell during the race, his dad told him he was still a winner for getting back up

   D. Austin was competing in the championships to win a trophy to make his dad proud

14. **Which of the following does the passage NOT explain?** (RL.5.1)

   A. Which events Austin was competing in

   B. Why Austin wanted to make his dad proud of him

   C. Which event Austin fell while competing in

   D. How tall Austin measured in height

15. **How does Austin's dad compare to Austin as an athlete?** (RL.5.3)

   A. Austin's dad was a track and field superstar athlete, just like Austin

   B. Austin was a more accomplished athlete than his father

   C. Austin's dad was a track and field superstar, while Austin struggled due to his height

   D. Austin used his height to his advantage, unlike his dad

16. **What challenge did Austin overcome in the passage?** (RL.5.2)

   A. Austin trained for the track and field championship meet

   B. Austin completed the 110-meter hurdle in record time

   C. Austin fell during the 110-meter hurdle event

   D. Austin had to overcome his nerves to compete in the championship meet

17. **Which paragraph(s) best describe(s) Austin's feelings?** (RL.5.1)

   A. Paragraph 3   **B.** Paragraph 4
   C. Paragraph 5   **D.** Paragraphs 4 and 5

1.4. CHAPTER REVIEW

1. READING: LITERATURE

18. **What can you infer about Austin's dad from the passage?** (RL.5.1)

    A. Austin's dad is disappointed in his son

    B. Austin's dad wishes his son was a better athlete

    C. Austin's dad knew that Austin needed to be encouraged after he fell during the hurdles event

    D. Austin's dad was shorter than Austin

19. **What is the main theme of the passage?** (RL.5.2)

    A. Admit defeat   **B.** Practice makes perfect

    C. Get back up after you fall   **D.** Challenge yourself

20. **Which line best describes why Austin struggled at athletics?** (RL.5.1)

    A. "Unfortunately for Austin, he was approximately 4 inches shorter in height."

    B. "In all three of his events, height was a major factor."

    C. "Because of this, it would be much harder for him to win."

    D. "Austin knew that he was going to struggle more than his dad did at his age."

21. **How do Austin's feelings change from paragraph 4 to paragraph 5?** (RL.5.3)

    A. In paragraph 4, Austin is nervous before the start of the race, and in paragraph 5, he is relieved when it is over

    B. In paragraph 4, Austin is upset before the start of the race, and in paragraph 5 he is happy his family was there to cheer him on

    C. In paragraph 4, Austin is nervous before the start of the race, and in paragraph 5, he is comforted by his dad's encouraging words

    D. In paragraph 4, Austin is upset before the start of the race, and in paragraph 5, he is embarrassed that he fell during the hurdle event

1. READING: LITERATURE

22. How do Austin and his dad interact in paragraph 5, at the end of the story? (RL.5.3)

    A. Austin and his dad shake hands after Austin wins a medal

    B. Austin's dad comforts him with encouragement and Austin smiles

    C. Austin's dad tries to make Austin smile, but Austin is embarrassed

    D. Austin and his dad share a hug as Austin's dad helps his son stand back up

TRUE OR FALSE

23. The main setting of the story is on the evening of a track and field championship meet. (RL.5.3)

    A. True   **B.** False

24. The line, "His primary focus was on training to excel at his events in time for the state championship track and field meet" lets the reader know that Austin was a determined athlete. (RL.5.1)

    A. True   **B.** False

> **Directions:** *Read the passages and answer the questions below. Choose the best answer.*

IN THE DAYS OF GIANTS

The oldest stories of every race of people tell about the Beginning of Things. But the various folk who first told them were so very different, the tales are so very old, and have changed so greatly in the telling from one generation to another, that there are almost as many accounts of the way in which the world began as there are nations upon the earth. So it is not strange that the people of the North have a legend of the Beginning quite different from that of the Southern, Eastern, and Western folk.

This book is made of the stories told by the Northern folk—the people who live in the land of the midnight sun, where summer is green

…continued next page

1.4. CHAPTER REVIEW

 prepaze

1. READING: LITERATURE

and pleasant, but winter is a terrible time of cold and gloom; where rocky mountains tower like huge giants, over whose heads the thunder rolls and crashes, and under whose feet are mines of precious metals. Therefore you will find the tales full of giants and dwarfs—spirits of the cold mountains and dark caverns.

You will find the hero to be Thor, with his thunderbolt hammer, who dwells in the happy heaven of Asgard, where All-Father Odin is king, and where Balder the beautiful makes springtime with his smile. In the north countries, winter, cold, and frost are very real and terrible enemies; while spring, sunshine, and warmth are near and dear friends. So the story of the Beginning of Things is a story of cold and heat, of the wicked giants who loved the cold, and of the good Æsir, who basked in pleasant warmth.

In the very Beginning of Things, the stories say, there were two worlds, one of burning heat and one of icy cold. The cold world was in the North, and from it flowed Elivâgar, a river of poisonous water, which hardened into ice and piled up into great mountains, filling the space which had no bottom. The other world in the South was on fire with a bright flame, a place of heat most terrible. And in those days through all space, there was nothing besides these two worlds of heat and cold.

But then began a fierce combat. Heat and cold met and strove to destroy each other, as they have tried to do ever since. Flaming sparks from the hot world fell upon the ice river which flowed from the place of cold. And though the bright sparks were quenched, in dying they wrought mischief, as they do to-day; for they melted the ice, which dripped and dripped like tears from the suffering world of cold. And then, wonderful to say, these chilly drops became alive; became a huge, breathing mass, a Frost-Giant with a wicked heart of ice. And he was the ancestor of all the giants who came afterwards, a bad and cruel race.

Gods and Heroes

When Jupiter became god and king of the whole world, he made his two brothers, Neptune and Pluto, kings under him. He made Neptune god and king of the sea: Pluto he made god and king of Hades. Hades was a world underground, in the middle of the earth, where men and women go and live when they die.

The next thing that Jupiter did was to marry Juno. Their wedding was the grandest and most wonderful that ever was seen. Invitations

...continued next page

www.prepaze.com

1. READING: LITERATURE

were sent out to all the gods and nymphs. The nymphs were a sort of fairy—some of them waited upon the goddesses; some of them lived in rivers, brooks, and trees. All of them came to the wedding, except one nymph named Chelone.

She refused to come: and, besides that, she laughed at the whole thing. When they told her that Jupiter was going to marry Juno, she laughed so loud that Jupiter himself could hear her. I don't know why she thought it so ridiculous, but I can guess pretty well. I expect she knew Juno's bad temper better than Jupiter did, and how Jupiter was just the sort of husband to spoil any wife's temper. But Jupiter was very

fond of Juno just then, and he did not like to be laughed at on his wedding day. So he had Chelone turned into a tortoise, so that she might never be able to laugh again. Nobody ever heard a tortoise laugh, nor ever will.

Jupiter and Juno set up their palace in the sky, just over the top of Mount Olympus, a high mountain in the north of Greece. And very soon, I am sorry to say, his quarrels with Juno began—so that, after all, poor Chelone had been right in not thinking much of the grand wedding. He always kept her for his Queen; but he cared for a great many Titanesses and nymphs much more than he did for her, and married more of them than anybody can reckon, one after another. This made Juno very angry, and they used to quarrel terribly. But something was going to happen which was almost as bad as quarreling, and which must have made Jupiter envy the peace and comfort of old Saturn, who had become only an earthly king.

The Titans made another war. And this time they got the help of the Giants, who were more terrible even than the Titans. They were immense monsters, some almost as tall as the tallest mountain, fearfully strong, and horribly ugly, with hair miles long, and rough beards down to their middle. One of them had fifty heads and a hundred hands.

...continued next page

prepaze

1. READING: LITERATURE

Another had serpents instead of legs. Others, called Cyclops, had only one eye, which was in the middle of their foreheads. But the most terrible of all was a giant named Typhon. He had a hundred heads, each like a dragon's, and darted flames from his mouth and eyes. A great battle was fought between the gods and the giants. The giants tried to get into the sky by piling up the mountains one upon another. They used oak-trees for clubs, and threw hills for stones. They set whole forests on fire, and tossed them up like torches to set fire to the sky. And at last Typhon's hundred fiery mouths set up a hundred different yells and roars all at once, so loud and horrible that Jupiter and all the gods ran away into Egypt and hid themselves there in the shapes of animals. Jupiter turned himself into a ram, and Juno became a cow.

25. **A myth is a type of traditional story that usually concerns a being, hero, or important event. Myths may or may not have a basis in fact or a natural explanation. Myths that are concerned with deities or demigods typically do not have a basis in fact. Myths sometimes explain some practice, rite, or phenomenon of nature. Which of the following is true about the passages?** (RL.5.9)

   A. Neither passage is a myth

   B. Both passages are myths

   C. The first passage is a myth but the second passage is not

   D. The second passage is a myth but the first passage is not

26. **In each passage, a war ensued. Which statement best describes the differences between the two wars?** (RL.5.9)

   A. The war in the first passage was a war between gods and humans, while the war in the second passage was between gods and other gods

   B. The war in the first passage was a war between elements (ice and fire), while the war in the second passage was between gods and Titans

   C. The war in the first passage was a war between gods and demigods, while the war in the second passage was between gods and humans

   D. The war in the first passage was a war between gods and other gods, while the war in the second passage was between elements

1. READING: LITERATURE

27. What role did giants play in the passages? (RL. 5.9)

A. Giants were the instigators of the wars in both of the passages

B. The first passage explains the origination of giants, while the second passage describes a war in which the giants fought alongside the Titans

C. The first passage described a war in which the giants fought against the gods, while the second passage described giants as peacemakers

D. The first passage explains the origination of giants, and there was no mention of giants in the second passage

> **Directions:** *Read the passage and answer the questions below. Choose the best answer.*

1.4. CHAPTER REVIEW

THE TALE OF JOHNNY TOWN-MOUSE

Johnny Town-mouse was born in a cupboard. Timmy Willie was born in a garden. Timmy Willie was a little country mouse who went to town by mistake in a hamper. The gardener sent vegetables to town once a week by the carrier; he packed them in a big hamper.

The gardener left the hamper by the garden gate so that the carrier could pick it up when he passed. Timmy Willie crept in through a hole in the wickerwork, and after eating some peas, Timmy Willie fell fast asleep.

He awoke in a fright, while the hamper was being lifted into the carrier's cart. Then there was a jolting, and a clattering of horse's feet; other packages were thrown in; for miles and miles—jolt—jolt—jolt! and Timmy Willie trembled amongst the jumbled-up vegetables.

At last, the cart stopped at a house, where the hamper was taken out, carried in, and set down. The cook gave the carrier sixpence; the back door banged, and the cart rumbled away. But there was no quiet; there seemed to be hundreds of carts passing. Dogs barked; boys whistled in the street; the cook laughed, the parlor maid ran up and down the stairs, and a canary sang like a steam engine.

...continued next page

 prepaze

1. READING: LITERATURE

Timmy Willie, who had lived all his life in a garden, was almost frightened to death. Presently the cook opened the hamper and began to unpack the vegetables. Out sprang the terrified Timmy Willie.

Up jumped the cook on a chair, exclaiming "A mouse! a mouse! Call the cat! Fetch me the poker, Sarah!" Timmy Willie did not wait for Sarah with the poker; he rushed along the skirting board till he came to a little hole, and in he popped.

He dropped half a foot, and crashed into the middle of a mouse dinner party, breaking three glasses. "Who in the world is this?" inquired Johnny Town-mouse. But after the first exclamation of surprise, he instantly recovered his manners.

With the utmost politeness, he introduced Timmy Willie to nine other mice, all with long tails and white neckties. Timmy Willie's own tail was insignificant. Johnny Town-mouse and his friends noticed it, but they were too well-bred to make personal remarks; only one of them asked Timmy Willie if he had ever been in a trap.

The dinner was of eight courses; not much of anything, but truly elegant. All the dishes were unknown to Timmy Willie, who would have been a little afraid of tasting them; only he was very hungry and very anxious to behave with company manners. The continual noise upstairs made him so nervous that he dropped a plate. "Never mind, they don't belong to us," said Johnny. "Why don't those youngsters come back with the dessert?"

It should be explained that two young mice, who were waiting on the others, went skirmishing upstairs to the kitchen between courses. Several times they had come tumbling in, squeaking and laughing; Timmy Willie learned with horror that they were being chased by the cat. His appetite failed, and he felt faint. "Try some jelly," said Johnny Town-mouse. "No? Would you rather go to bed? I will show you a most comfortable sofa pillow."

The sofa pillow had a hole in it. Johnny Town-mouse quite honestly recommended it as the best bed, kept exclusively for visitors. But the sofa smelled of a cat. Timmy Willie preferred to spend a miserable night under the fender.

...continued next page

1. READING: LITERATURE

It was just the same next day. An excellent breakfast was provided (for mice accustomed to eating bacon), but Timmy Willie had been reared on roots and salad. Johnny Town-mouse and his friends racketed about under the floors and came boldly out all over the house in the evening. One particularly loud crash was caused by Sarah tumbling downstairs with the tea-tray; there were crumbs and sugar and smears of jam to be collected, in spite of the cat.

Timmy Willie longed to be at home in his peaceful nest in a sunny bank. The food disagreed with him; the noise prevented him from sleeping. In a few days, he grew so thin that Johnny Town-mouse noticed it and questioned him. He listened to Timmy Willie's story and inquired about the garden. "It sounds rather a dull place. What do you do when it rains?"

"When it rains, I sit in my little sandy burrow and shell corn and seeds from my autumn store. I peep out at the throstles and blackbirds on the lawn, and my friend Cock Robin. And when the sun comes out again, you should see my garden and the flowers—roses and pinks and pansies—no noise except the birds and bees, and the lambs in the meadows."

"There goes that cat again!" exclaimed Johnny Town-mouse. When they had taken refuge in the coal-cellar he resumed the conversation; "I confess I am a little disappointed; we have endeavored to entertain you, Timothy William."

"Oh yes, yes, you have been most kind; but I do feel so ill," said Timmy Willie.

"It may be that your teeth and digestion are unaccustomed to our food; perhaps it might be wiser for you to return in the hamper."

"Oh? Oh!" cried Timmy Willie.

"Why of course for the matter of that we could have sent you back last week," said Johnny rather huffily—"did you not know that the hamper goes back empty on Saturdays?"

So, Timmy Willie said good-bye to his new friends, and hid in the hamper with a crumb of cake and a withered cabbage leaf; and after much jolting, he was set down safely in his own garden.

 prepaze

1. READING: LITERATURE

28. Which of the following would be the best illustration to use as the cover of this book? (RL. 5.7)

A.

B.

C.

D.

29. What part of the story is illustrated in the following image? (RL. 5.7)

A. "Presently the cook opened the hamper and began to unpack the vegetables."

B. "Timmy Willie trembled amongst the jumbled-up vegetables."

C. "So, Timmy Willie said good-bye to his new friends, and hid in the hamper with a crumb of the cake."

D. "'There goes that cat again!' exclaimed Johnny Town-mouse."

1. READING: LITERATURE

30. Which part of the story is best illustrated in the following picture? (RL. 5.7)

A. "Up jumped the cook on a chair, exclaiming 'A mouse! a mouse! Call the cat! Fetch me the poker, Sarah!'"

B. "Johnny Town-mouse was born in a cupboard. Timmy Willie was born in a garden."

C. "Timmy Willie crept in through a hole in the wickerwork, and after eating some peas, Timmy Willie fell fast asleep."

D. "He dropped half a foot and crashed into the middle of a mouse dinner party, breaking three glasses."

prepaze

2. READING: INFORMATIONAL TEXT

2.1. **KEY IDEAS AND DETAILS**   **68**
   ❖ Quote Accurately from a Text
   ❖ Determine Main Ideas and Key Details
   ❖ Explain Relationships

3.2. **CRAFT AND STRUCTURE**   **75**
   ❖ Word Meanings
   ❖ Text Structure
   ❖ Analyze Differences in Point of View

4.3. **INTEGRATION OF KNOWLEDGE AND IDEAS**   **83**
   ❖ Demonstrate the Ability to Locate an Answer
      to a Question Quickly
   ❖ Supporting Evidence
   ❖ Integrate Information from Several Texts

2.4. **CHAPTER REVIEW**   **92**

2. READING: INFORMATIONAL TEXT

2.1. Key Ideas and Details

Common Core State Standards: CCSS.ELA-LITERACY.RI.5.1, CCSS.ELA-LITERACY.RI.5.2, CCSS. ELA-LITERACY.RI.5.3

Skills:

- Quote accurately from a text when explaining what the text says explicitly and when drawing inferences from the text.
- Determine two or more main ideas of a text and explain how they are supported by key details; summarize the text.
- Explain the relationships or interactions between two or more individuals, events, ideas, or concepts in a historical, scientific, or technical text based on specific information in the text.

> **Directions:** *Read the text and answer the questions below.*

APACHES

What was it like to be an Apache?

The Apache, one of the most famous Native American groups, have lived in North America for more than 600 years. In the 19th century, the Apache were among the greatest horse riders in the country. Unlike European settlers, the Apache did not bother with saddles. Instead, they rode bareback. Instead of staying in one place and building cities, the Apache were nomadic and liked to move around. As the seasons changed, the Apache would change with them. They would go to one place to hunt and another to look for fruits and nuts to eat. They would go to one place for the summer and another for the winter. Although they never stayed in one place for very long, the Apache had a great connection to the land.

...continued next page

2. READING: INFORMATIONAL TEXT

Where did they sleep?

There were three different kinds of Apache houses: the teepee, the wickiup, and the hogan. Teepees are cone-shaped tents made from wooden frames. They could be taken down whenever it was time to move from one place to another. These were used by Apache living on the plains. Wickiups and hogans were more permanent than teepees. Wickiups were 8-foot-tall wooden frames covered in brush. Hogans were made of mud or clay. They were used for shelter during the winter when it was cold. The thick earthen walls kept the Apache warm when it was too cold for life on the plains.

What is Apache life like today?

In the late 1800s, the Apache fought a series of wars against the United States Army. Led by great warriors like Geronimo and Cochise, they fought for years to protect their way of life. But the United States Army was too strong for them and gradually forced the Apache onto reservations in New Mexico and Arizona. Today, Apache people on those reservations work to maintain their ancient culture. Though they are proud of their past, they lead modern lives. There are Apache all over the country, from New York to Los Angeles.

2.1. KEY IDEAS AND DETAILS

═══════════════ **MULTIPLE CHOICE** ═══════════════

1. **What can you infer about the Apache from the text ?** (RI.5.1)
   - **A.** They did not use horses to travel
   - **B.** They moved from one location to another quite often
   - **C.** They are the oldest Native American tribe in the U.S.
   - **D.** They were farmers

2. **What is one main idea from the text?** (RI.5.2)
   - **A.** The Apache ate fruits and nuts
   - **B.** The Apache were led by great warriors like Geronimo and Cochise
   - **C.** The Apache slept in three different types of housing
   - **D.** The Apache did not use saddles on their horses

2. READING: INFORMATIONAL TEXT

3. Which is not a key detail from the text? (RI.5.2)

   A. Teepees could be taken down and moved from one place to another

   B. Winters were harsh

   C. The Apache fought a series of wars against the U.S. Army

   D. The Apache have lived in the U.S. for more than 600 years

4. Compare teepees to wickiups. (RI.5.3)

   A. Teepees and wickiups were both made from wooden frames

   B. Teepees and wickiups were permanent structures

   C. Teepees were covered in mud and wickiups were covered in brush

   D. Teepees and wickiups were shaped like rectangles

5. What does the text not explain? (RI.5.1)

   A. Exactly when the Apache moved from one place to another

   B. How long the Apache have been in the U.S

   C. What life is like for the Apache today

   D. What the wooden frames on teepees were covered with

6. Which line best describes the lifestyle of the Apache? (RL.5.1)

   A. "Instead of staying in one place and building cities, the Apache were nomadic and liked to move around."

   B. "As the seasons changed, the Apache would change with them."

   C. "They would go one place to hunt and another to look for fruits and nuts to eat."

   D. "They would go one place for the summer and another for the winter."

7. Which sentence below best summarizes the text? (RI.5.2)

   A. The Apache were nomadic and liked to move around

   B. The Apache have a rich culture in the U.S. that dates back more than 600 years

   C. The Apache slept in teepees, wickiups, and hogans

   D. The Apache now live all over the U.S.

2. READING: INFORMATIONAL TEXT

8. **How do the Apache of today compare to those in the 19th century?** (RI.5.3)

    A. Both ride horses as their main mode of transportation

    B. Both live in large U.S. cities

    C. Both work to maintain their ancient culture

    D. Both are nomadic and like to move around

9. **Why were hogans built with mud or clay?** (RI.5.3)

    A. They were used for shelter during the winter when it was cold

    B. The thick earthen walls would keep Apache warm

    C. They were tall structures that provided more room

    D. A and B

10. **What relationship did the Apaches have to the seasons?** (RI.5.3)

    A. They depended on the seasons for many things

    B. They moved according to the seasons

    C. The ate and hunted for different food sources based on the season

    D. B and C

> ➤ **Directions:** *Read the text and answer the questions below.*

2.1. KEY IDEAS AND DETAILS

ADAPTATIONS IN THE RAINFOREST

Tropical rainforests have ideal climates for plant growth. Tropical rainforests are hot, humid, and wet. They have abundant rainfall and are warm year-round. Temperatures range from about 85 degrees Fahrenheit during the day to 70 at night. Tropical rainforests get at least 80 inches of rainfall each year. These two factors also create challenges for the plants that live there. As a result, plants in tropical rainforests have adapted to these conditions by making adjustments in how they grow.

...continued next page

2. READING: INFORMATIONAL TEXT

The perfect conditions for plant life—warm temperatures and plenty of water—cause plants to grow quickly. One consequence of rapid plant growth is the depletion of nutrients in the soil. It also creates a thick layer of leaves in the upper part of the forest (the canopy) that blocks sunlight from reaching the forest floor. Most plants get their nutrients, water, and oxygen from the soil. However, in the rainforest, where the soil is not nutrient-rich, many plants don't rely on it as their source of food. Some plants, called epiphytes, or air plants, have learned to get water and nutrients from the air. Some examples of epiphytes in rainforests are mosses, lichens, and orchids. Although they often live on other plants, they don't take any nutrients from them—they get what they need straight from the air with special root systems.

Other plants that grow on plants actually DO take nutrients from that plant. They are called parasitic plants, and the plant they grow on is called a host plant. Instead of getting food and water from the soil, parasitic plants have developed roots that cling to a host plant, pierce through its leaves, stem, or trunk, and suck the nutrients out of the host. An example of a parasitic plant you might know is mistletoe. Parasitic plants can kill their host plant if they grow too rapidly. However, they tend to *not* kill their host plant, because without a host, the parasitic plant will also die.

11. **What can you infer about rainforests?** (RI.5.1)
   A. Rainforests have a consistently warm climate
   B. Rainforests don't have many animals that live in them
   C. Rainforests are primarily located on one continent
   D. Plants grow slowly due to the hot temperatures in rainforests

12. **What is one main idea of the text?** (RI.5.2)
   A. Plants need nutrients to stay alive
   B. Plants have overcome challenges by developing adaptations
   C. Rainforests have a range of temperatures
   D. Rainforests are decreasing in size

2. READING: INFORMATIONAL TEXT

13. Which line best describes why plants can survive in the rainforest? (RI.5.1)

- **A.** "As a result, plants in tropical rainforests have adapted to these conditions by making adjustments in how they grow."
- **B.** "The perfect conditions for plant life—warm temperatures and plenty of water—cause plants to grow quickly."
- **C.** "One consequence of rapid plant growth is the depletion of nutrients in the soil."
- **D.** "Most plants get their nutrients, water, and oxygen from the soil."

14. How do epiphytes compare to parasitic plants? (RI.5.3)

- **A.** Epiphytes and parasitic plants get their nutrients from other plants
- **B.** Epiphytes get their nutrients from the air, while parasitic plants get their nutrients from other plants
- **C.** Epiphytes get their nutrients from other plants, while parasitic plants get their nutrients from the air
- **D.** Epiphytes and parasitic plants get their nutrients from the air

15. How would you summarize the text? (RI.5.2)

- **A.** Rainforests are endangered due to having too many plants
- **B.** Plants grow quickly in rainforests due to the warm temperatures and heavy rainfall, which cause plants to adapt
- **C.** Plants have to get nutrients from other plants to survive
- **D.** The canopy in a rainforest protects the plants below

16. How do plants react to the conditions of the rainforest? (RI.5.3)

- **A.** Because of the heavy rainfall in a rainforest, plants grow quickly
- **B.** Because of the warm temperatures in a rainforest, plants grow quickly
- **C.** Because of the perfect weather conditions in a rainforest, plants grow quickly
- **D.** All of the above

2.1. KEY IDEAS AND DETAILS

2. READING: INFORMATIONAL TEXT

17. **What is a second main idea of the text?** (RI.5.2)

    A. "One consequence of rapid plant growth is the depletion of nutrients in the soil."

    B. "A parasitic plant you might know is mistletoe."

    C. "Temperatures range from about 85 degrees Fahrenheit during the day to 70 at night."

    D. "Some examples of epiphytes in rainforests are mosses, lichens, and orchids."

18. **Which paragraph(s) best describe(s) plant adaptations?** (RI.5.1)

    A. Paragraph 1   **B.** Paragraph 2

    C. Paragraph 3   **D.** Paragraph 2 and 3

19. **In which way(s) is/are mosses and orchids similar?** (RI.5.3)

    A. Both plants are epiphytes

    B. Both plants get their nutrients from the air

    C. Both plants are parasitic plants

    D. A and B

20. **What does the passage NOT explain?** (RI.5.1)

    A. The temperature of rainforests

    B. The difference between epiphytes and parasitic plants

    C. More than one adaptation for plants in the rainforest

    D. The perfect conditions for plant life

2.2. CRAFT AND STRUCTURE

2. READING: INFORMATIONAL TEXT

~ 2.2. Craft and Structure ~

Common Core State Standards: CCSS.ELA-LITERACY.RI.5.4, CCSS.ELA-LITERACY.RI.5.5, CCSS.ELA-LITERACY.RI.5.6

Skills:

- Determine the meaning of general academic and domain-specific words and phrases in a text.
- Compare and contrast the overall structure of events, ideas, concepts, or information in two or more texts.
- Analyze multiple accounts of the same event or topic, noting important similarities and differences in the point of view they represent.

> **Directions:** *Read the passage and answer the questions below.*

IN THEIR OWN CORNER OF THE ANTARCTIC, THESE PENGUINS ARE LIVING LIFE

Giant colonies of penguins have recently been discovered near the Antarctic **Peninsula**. The colonies are home to over 1.5 million birds, about the **population** of Philadelphia, the sixth-largest U.S. city.

The area is an important sanctuary, protecting the animals from humans as well as man-made changes in the weather.

Scientists are now calling for the zone to be safeguarded by a marine wildlife reserve. The reserve is currently **under consideration.**

The Adélie penguin colonies were discovered on the Danger Islands in the Weddell Sea. This area is on the eastern part of the Antarctic Peninsula. The Antarctic Peninsula is where **the continent reaches** closest to Chile and Argentina, at the southern tip of South America. It is hard to access and has few human visitors.

 prepaze

2. READING: INFORMATIONAL TEXT

===== **MULTIPLE CHOICE** =====

1. **What does the word *peninsula* most likely mean?** (RI.5.4)

    A. a type of bird   **B.** a piece of land
    C. a city building   **D.** a type of farm

2. **What does the word *population* most likely mean?** (RI.5.4)

    A. a type of map   **B.** a type of weather
    C. the number of bird species   **D.** the number of residents

3. **What does the phrase *the continent reaches* most likely mean?** (RI.5.4)

    A. the continent is closely located next to Chile and Argentina
    B. the continent is most similar to Chile and Argentina
    C. the continent has a hand that reaches out and touches Chile and Argentina
    D. the continent is larger than Chile and Argentina

4. **What does the phrase *under consideration* most likely mean?** (RI.5.4)

    A. under construction   **B.** being thought about
    C. inconsiderate   **D.** being misunderstood

> **Directions:** *Read the passage and answer the questions below.*

PASSAGE 1

There are hundreds of dog breeds all over the world. Each breed of dog has its own set of characteristics. Dogs differ in appearance, personality, and function based on their breeds. For example, some dogs are considered companion dogs while others are considered hunting dogs.

Dogs such as Great Danes and Scottish Deerhounds are extremely large. Chihuahuas and Yorkshire Terriers, on the other hand, are very small dogs. Dogs also have a wide range of temperaments. Some dogs are affectionate and gentle, which makes them good domestic pets. Wild, vicious dogs are not recommended to live in homes. Breed research makes it easy to identify the features and roles of specific dogs.

...continued next page

2. READING: INFORMATIONAL TEXT

PASSAGE 2

Dogs are special pets, because they make good companions. They are extremely friendly, not only with humans but with other dogs as well. Science has shown that dogs are naturally social animals. They have specific genes that cause this friendly behavior. That is what makes them unique. They are genetically programmed to be playful and affectionate. That is why people who want pets should consider dogs; they are the best pets in the world.

=== MULTIPLE CHOICE ===

5. Which answer best describes the text structure in Passage 1? (RI.5.5)

A. cause and effect **B.** sequence
C. compare and contrast **D.** problem and solution

6. Which answer best describes the text structure in Passage 2? (RI.5.5)

A. chronological **B.** compare and contrast
C. descriptive **D.** cause and effect

7. What is the main similarity between these two passages? (RI.5.5, RI.5.6)

A. These passages share the same topic
B. These passages share the same structure
C. These passages tell the same story
D. These passages describe the same chronological event

8. What is the main difference between these two passages? (RI.5.5, RI.5.6)

A. Passage 1 is a narrative text; Passage 2 is an informational text
B. Passage 1 is an informational text; Passage 2 is a persuasive text
C. Passage 1 is a chronological text; Passage 2 is a persuasive text
D. Passage 1 is an informational text; Passage 2 is a narrative text

2.2. CRAFT AND STRUCTURE

 prepaze

2. READING: INFORMATIONAL TEXT

> **Directions:** *Read the passage and answer the questions below.*

PASSAGE 1

Last summer, I visited the Grand Canyon. First, I went sightseeing. I was amazed by the breathtaking view and beautiful atmosphere. Next, I visited the historic Watchtower. The Watchtower offers a wide view that extends for nearly hundreds of miles. It was astounding! Lastly, I enjoyed hiking and rafting near the Grand Canyon. These are just a few of the reasons why visiting the Grand Canyon is a wonderful experience.

PASSAGE 2

The Grand Canyon is an American National Park located in the state of Arizona. It spans 18 miles across at its widest point, and is about 6,000 feet deep. Although it is not the largest canyon in the world, the Grand Canyon is considered to be one of the seven wonders of the natural world. Approximately five million visitors flock to this popular tourist destination every year.

2.2. CRAFT AND STRUCTURE

=== MULTIPLE CHOICE ===

9. **Which statement best describes the difference in the structure of Passage 1 and Passage 2?** (RI.5.5)

   A. Passage 1 is a chronological text, while passage 2 is a descriptive text

   B. Passage 1 is a cause/effect text, while passage 2 is a problem/solution text

   C. Passage 1 is a narrative text, while passage 2 is a chronological text

   D. Passage 1 is a descriptive text, while passage 2 is a narrative text

2. READING: INFORMATIONAL TEXT

10. **Which statement best describes the difference in the point of view of Passage 1 and Passage 2?** (RI.5.6)

    A. Passage 1 is written in the third person, while Passage 2 is written in the second person

    B. Passage 1 is written in the first person, while Passage 2 is written in the third person

    C. Passage 1 is written in the first person, while Passage 2 is written in the second person

    D. Passage 1 is written in the second person, while Passage 2 is written in the third person

11. **Which statement best describes the similarities between Passage 1 and Passage 2?** (RI.5.6)

    A. Both passages offer an opinion about the Grand Canyon

    B. Both passages describe the Grand Canyon's appearance

    C. Both passages explain what caused the formation of the Grand Canyon

    D. Both passages tell a story about the Grand Canyon

12. **What is most likely the meaning of the underlined word?** (RI.5.4)

    I was amazed by the breathtaking view and beautiful <u>atmosphere</u>.

    A. Surroundings   **B.** Breath

    C. Activities   **D.** Tourism

➤ **Directions:** *Read the passage and answer the questions below.*

Sneaky Marketing: School Reward Programs Push Junk Food, Experts Say

Critics do not object to schools getting much-needed **funds**. But they do protest the nutritional **quality** of foods in rewards programs. They say many of the products are not healthy. This could result in a lifelong preference for unhealthy foods.

...continued next page

 prepaze

2. READING: INFORMATIONAL TEXT

Box Tops is the most popular of the programs. Researchers at Harvard University did a study of it. The study found that two out of every three products in the Box Tops program do not meet the government's nutrition guidelines for sale in schools. That means they are not healthy enough to be sold in school cafeterias.

"The vast majority of these products can't be sold in schools," Schwartz said. "So they shouldn't be **advertised** in schools."

The companies also argue that the program is designed for the parents, not their children. It is parents who do the food shopping, after all. But critics say children are often highly **involved** in rewards programs. Schools often advertise the programs directly to students, they say.

=== **MULTIPLE CHOICE** ===

13. What does the word *funds* most likely mean? (RI.5.4)

A. Attention   **B.** Labels
C. Money   **D.** Food

14. What does the word *quality* most likely mean? (RI.5.4)

A. Amount   **B.** Value
C. Flavor   **D.** Cost

15. What does the word *advertised* most likely mean? (RI.5.4)

A. Marketed   **B.** Eaten
C. Stored   **D.** Argued

16. What does the word *involved* most likely mean? (RI.5.4)

A. Shared   **B.** Complaining
C. Unsuccessful   **D.** Participating

2. READING: INFORMATIONAL TEXT

> **Directions:** *Read the passage and answer the questions below.*

HOW DOES FLUORIDE WORK?

1 Fluoride is a natural element found in the earth's crust as well as in water and air. Decades ago, scientists discovered that kids who naturally had more fluoride in their drinking water had fewer cavities. In the mid-1940s, communities started to put more fluoride in their water supply to protect people against tooth decay.

2 Fluoride helps because when teeth are growing, it mixes with tooth enamel — that hard coating on your teeth. That prevents tooth decay, or cavities. But fluoride can help even after your teeth are formed. It works with saliva to protect tooth enamel from plaque and sugars. By using fluoride toothpaste, for instance, everyone can enjoy some cavity protection. Fewer cavities means healthier teeth when you're an adult — and less chance of having to wear false teeth (dentures) when you're old!

=== MULTIPLE CHOICE ===

17. Which answer best describes the text structure found in Paragraph 1? (RI.5.5)

A. Narrative
B. Chronological
C. Descriptive
D. Compare/contrast

18. Which answer best describes the text structure found in Paragraph 2? (RI.5.5)

A. Cause/effect
B. Narrative
C. Chronological
D. Compare/contrast

 prepaze

2.2. CRAFT AND STRUCTURE

2. READING: INFORMATIONAL TEXT

19. **Which statement best explain how the paragraphs are similar?** (RI.5.5)

   A. Both paragraphs share the same text structure

   B. Both paragraphs share the same topic

   C. Both paragraphs compare and contrast the two subjects

   D. Both paragraphs present a problem and a solution

20. **Which statement best explains how the paragraphs are different?** (RI.5.5)

   A. The text structure of Paragraph 1 differs from Paragraph 2

   B. The subtopic of Paragraph 1 differs from Paragraph 2

   C. The author of Paragraph 1 differs from Paragraph 2

   D. There are no differences found in these paragraphs

2.3. INTEGRATION OF KNOWLEDGE AND IDEAS

2. READING: INFORMATIONAL TEXT

∿ 2.3. Integration of Knowledge and Ideas ∿

Common Core State Standards: CCSS.ELA–LITERACY.RI.5.7, CCSS.ELA–LITERACY.RI.5.9

Skills:

- Draw on information from multiple print or digital sources, demonstrating the ability to locate an answer to a question quickly or to solve a problem efficiently.
- Integrate information from several texts on the same topic or in order to write or speak about the subject knowledgeably.

> ➢ **Directions:** *Look at the picture and read the passages. Then answer the questions below.*

	Black Bear	Grizzly Bear
Shoulder:	No hump	Hump
Ears:	Taller	Short and rounded
Face:	Straight profile	Dished profile
Front Claws:	Dark ~ 1.5" long	Light ~ 2-4" long

 prepaze

2. READING: INFORMATIONAL TEXT

GRIZZLY BEARS

Grizzly bears are large, brown bears. An adult grizzly is usually larger than an adult black bear. The footprint of a grizzly bear will have more of a square shape than a black bear's footprint. Grizzly bears eat the most food during autumn, while preparing for hibernation. Sometimes they eat close to 100 pounds of food in one day!

AMERICAN BLACK BEAR

Black bears spend the winter holed up in caves, burrows, and other protected retreats such as large openings in trees or brush piles. They survive through their immense body fat that they generate by eating large amounts in the warmer months. Black bears can be found anywhere from Canada to northern Mexico, and their hibernation period is often determined by their location.

=== MULTIPLE CHOICE ===

1. **How could these resources be helpful if you were looking for information about bears?** (RI.5.7, RI.5.9)

   A. The information explains the difference between black bears and grizzly bears

   B. The information explains how there are 8 different bear species

   C. The information explains the similarities between panda bears and polar bears

   D. The information explains how bears are natural hunters

2. **Which of the following resources would best accompany this information?** (RI.5.7, RI.5.9)

   A. An article about a bear exhibit at the local zoo

   B. A textbook about polar animals eating habits

   C. A website about how to prevent bear attacks

   D. A website about bear appearances and characteristics

2. READING: INFORMATIONAL TEXT

3. **How could the picture be helpful if you were looking for information about bears?** (RI.5.7, RI.5.9)

    A. The picture shows bears hibernating in the winter

    B. The picture shows bears in their natural habitats

    C. The picture shows physical details about bears

    D. The picture shows geographical details about bears

4. **Which of these questions is NOT addressed in the passages?** (RI.5.7, RI.5.9)

    A. What do grizzly bears eat?

    B. Where do black bears live?

    C. Do grizzly bears have humps?

    D. Do black bears hibernate?

> **Directions:** *Read the passages and answer the questions below.*

PASSAGE 1
COUNTRIES OF THE WORLD: HONDURAS

Honduras is the second largest country in Central America, following Nicaragua. It shares borders with Guatemala, Nicaragua and El Salvador. In the north, the country boasts a vast coastline along the Caribbean Sea. In the south, it shares a small stretch with the Pacific Ocean. The country also has several islands off its coasts.

Honduras has four distinct regions. They are the central highlands, Pacific lowlands, eastern Caribbean lowlands and northern coastal plains. The country has many mountains, with peaks as high as 9,347 feet. It is the only country in Central America without volcanoes.

PASSAGE 2
HONDURAS: CULTURE & HISTORY

Spanish is the principal language and is spoken throughout the country, although English (spoken with a broad Caribbean accent) is the language of choice in the Bay Islands. The remaining indigenous tribes have their own distinct languages.

...continued next page

2.3. INTEGRATION OF KNOWLEDGE AND IDEAS

2. READING: INFORMATIONAL TEXT

Honduran crafts include woodcarving (notably wooden instruments), basketry, embroidery, textile arts, leather craft, and ceramics. The country's cuisine is based around beans, rice, tortillas, fried bananas, meat, potatoes, cream, and cheese.

2.3. INTEGRATION OF KNOWLEDGE AND IDEAS

MULTIPLE CHOICE

5. **How do both texts help to develop the topic?** (RI.5.7, RI.5.9)

   A. Both texts offer tips about food and language in Honduras

   B. Both texts describe the location of Honduras

   C. Both texts state facts about Honduras

   D. Both texts express an opinion about Honduras

6. **Which of the following topics could you learn about from reading Passage 1?** (RI.5.7, RI.5.9)

   A. The four regions of Honduras   **B.** Celebrations in Honduras
   C. Animal habitats in Honduras   **D.** The discovery of Honduras

7. **Which passage would be the most helpful if you were looking for information about popular hobbies in Honduras?** (RI.5.7, RI.5.9)

   A. Passage 1   **B.** Passage 2
   C. Both passages   **D.** None of the above

8. **Which passage would be the most helpful if you were looking for information about countries surrounding Honduras?** (RI.5.7, RI.5.9)

   A. Passage 1   **B.** Passage 2
   C. Both passages   **D.** None of the above

2. READING: INFORMATIONAL TEXT

> **Directions:** *Read the passage and look at the chart. Then answer the questions below.*

THE AIR WE BREATHE

Utah has long been known for its beautiful mountains and landscapes. Unfortunately, it is now also known for its poor air quality. Experts are currently working on solutions, but at the moment Utah is choking under the weight of three primary sources of pollution: Mobile sources (vehicle emissions), Point Sources (mostly industrial emissions), and Area Sources (building emissions).

Mobile sources include emissions from cars, trucks, airplanes, and even lawnmowers! These vehicle emissions are responsible for 57% of air pollution in the state. It's up to us, the residents of Utah, to cut down on these harmful emissions through carpooling and public transportation.

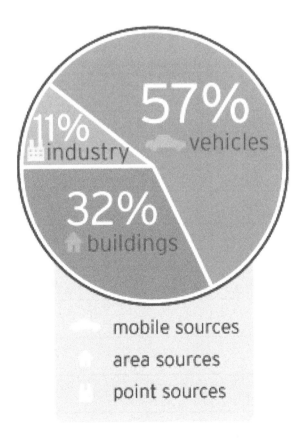

mobile sources

area sources

point sources

2. READING: INFORMATIONAL TEXT

FILL IN THE BLANK

9. According to the text, there are three categories
    of _____ **sources.** (RI.5.7)

10. According to the chart, 32% of pollution comes from buildings,
    or _____ **sources.** (RI.5.7)

FREE RESPONSE

11. **Explain how both the chart and the text can be used to explain
    sources of pollution.** (RI.5.7)

    _____

    _____

    _____

    _____

    _____

    _____

    _____

    _____

    _____

    _____

    _____

    _____

2. READING: INFORMATIONAL TEXT

> **Directions:** *Read the passages and answer the questions below.*

TRICERATOPS

The Triceratops was the last and largest of the horned dinosaurs. It may have been one of the most common dinosaurs in the North American West at the time of Tyrannosaurus rex. These dinosaurs are often pictured traveling in large groups, but the biggest gathering ever found consisted of three youngsters. Perhaps it lived only in family groups. The Triceratops nipped at low-growing plants with its beak and cut them with its 800 little teeth. When walking, the Triceratops's toes pointed outward, a primitive posture common to most dinosaurs. Given its multi-ton weight, it did not walk quickly.

TRICERATOPS DINOSAURS

Triceratops was and herbivores, meaning it ate plants, not animals. It probably ate many varieties of plants and may have used its large bulk and strength to knock down trees in order to get at leaves, just like a current day elephant. Triceratops had rows and rows of teeth as well as a sharp hard beak, allowing it to slice and crush all sorts of vegetation. Despite its fearsome appearance, it didn't kill other dinosaurs for meat. However, it likely would have defended itself well from predators. It is thought that the Triceratops wandered the plains on all fours eating plants as it went, sort of like buffalo or cows do today.

prepaze

NAME: .... DATE: ....

2. READING: INFORMATIONAL TEXT

2.3. INTEGRATION OF KNOWLEDGE AND IDEAS

==================== **MULTIPLE CHOICE** ====================

12. **What kind of information could you find in these two texts?** (RI.5.7, RI.5.9)

  A. Information about the Triceratops's eggs

  B. Information about the Triceratops's diet

  C. Information about Triceratops fossils

  D. Information about a Triceratops exhibit

13. **Which of the following topics is NOT found in these texts?** (RI.5.7, RI.5.9)

  A. Triceratops toe position

  B. Triceratops teeth

  C. Triceratops size and weight

  D. Triceratops skin and scales

14. **Which of the following texts would best accompany this information?** (RI.5.7, RI.5.9)

  A. An encyclopedia page about Triceratops

  B. A dictionary page about Triceratops

  C. A fictional novel about a Triceratops adventure

  D. None of the above

15. **Which of the following digital sources would best accompany this information?** (RI.5.7, RI.5.9)

  A. A documentary video about Triceratops

  B. A website about Triceratops discoveries

  C. An image of a Triceratops skeleton

  D. All of the above

==================== **TRUE OR FALSE** ====================

16. **It is best to limit your resources to one text per topic.** (RI.5.9)

  A. True   **B.** False

2. READING: INFORMATIONAL TEXT

17. **Both a magazine article and a website can be used to find information about flowers.** (RI.5.7)

    A. True   **B.** False

18. **An internet keyword search can be a quick way to find answers.** (RI.5.7)

    A. True   **B.** False

19. **A thesaurus would be the best resource for locating a map of Australia.** (RI.5.7)

    A. True   **B.** False

20. **Two texts written by different authors will always offer conflicting information.** (RI.5.9)

    A. True   **B.** False

2.3. INTEGRATION OF KNOWLEDGE AND IDEAS

2.4. CHAPTER REVIEW

2. READING: INFORMATIONAL TEXT

2.4. Chapter Review

> **Directions:** *Read the passages and answer the questions below.*

PASSAGE 1

AFRICAN-AMERICAN CIVIL RIGHTS MOVEMENT

The end of the Civil War also brought the end of slavery, but the fight for equal rights for African-Americans was far from over. The South continued to discriminate against African-Americans, and implemented the Jim Crow laws. These laws enforced segregation between whites and blacks. They required African Americans to attend different schools, eat at different restaurants, and even made them use separate restrooms. They also restricted African-American voting rights.

An activist for African American Civil Rights was Rosa Parks, an ordinary woman who became famous in 1955 for refusing to give up her bus seat to a white man. This led to the Montgomery Bus Boycott.

PASSAGE 2

ABBY TAKES A STAND: 1960

Abby and Mama sat right up front. There was no need to go to the back of the bus any longer. It was 1960. Black people could sit wherever they wanted on public buses. But in many ways blacks and whites were as separate as ever. Abby and Patsy still attended an all-black school. Folks couldn't get certain jobs. Nobody could live in a white neighborhood. Theaters, hotels, amusement parks and restaurants all over town had awful signs: WHITES ONLY. All except for the Nashville Public Library. Abby and Patsy went there often.

2. READING: INFORMATIONAL TEXT

=== **MULTIPLE CHOICE** ===

1. **What is the common topic in both of these passages?** (RI.5.5, RI.5.6)

   A. The Civil Rights Movement
   B. Bus segregation
   C. Neighborhood segregation
   D. All of the above

2. **Which statement best describes how these passages differ in text structure?** (RI.5.5)

   A. Passage 1 describes segregation laws, while Passage 2 tells a story about characters living in that era

   B. Passage 1 tells a story about segregation, while Passage 2 describes historical events

   C. Passage 1 presents a chronological timeline about segregation, while Passage 2 tells a story about characters living in that era

   D. Passage 1 describes segregation laws, while Passage 1 presents a chronological timeline

3. **Which statement best describes both the similarities and differences between these passages?** (RI.5.5, RI.5.6)

   A. Both passages describe the same events, but from different points of view

   B. Both passages share the same point of view, but describe different events

   C. Both passages share the same text structure, but describe different events

   D. Both passages describe the same events, from the same point of view

4. **What is most likely the meaning of the underlined word?** (RI.5.4)

   The South continued to discriminate against African-Americans, and

   <u>implemented</u> the Jim Crow laws.

   A. Reduced
   B. Enforced
   C. Reported
   D. Inspected

 prepaze

2. READING: INFORMATIONAL TEXT

=== **TRUE OR FALSE** ===

5. **Academic word meanings can found through text evidence.** (RI.5.4)

    A. True   **B.** False

6. **Both the compare/contrast and the problem/solution text structures explore two or more parts of a subject.** (RI.5.5)

    A. True   **B.** False

7. **Multiple accounts of the same event must be presented from the same point of view.** (RI.5.6)

    A. True   **B.** False

8. **A narrative text will always differ in both structure and point of view when compared to an informational text.** (RI.5.5, RI.5.6)

    A. True   **B.** False

> ➤ **Directions:** *Read the passages and answer the questions below.*

TRICERATOPS

The Triceratops was the last and largest of the horned dinosaurs. It may have been one of the most common dinosaurs in the North American West at the time of Tyrannosaurus rex. These dinosaurs are often pictured traveling in large groups, but the biggest gathering of Triceratops ever found consisted of three youngsters. Perhaps it lived only in family groups. The Triceratops nipped at low-growing plants with its beak and cut them with its 800 little teeth. When walking, the Triceratops's toes pointed outward, a primitive posture common to most dinosaurs. Given its multi-ton weight, it did not walk quickly.

...continued next page

2. READING: INFORMATIONAL TEXT

TRICERATOPS DINOSAURS

Triceratops were herbivores, meaning they ate plants and not animals or meat. They probably ate many varieties of plants and may have used their large bulk and strength to knock down trees in order to get at leaves like current day elephants. The Triceratops had rows and rows of teeth as well as a sharp hard beak, allowing them to slice and crush all sorts of vegetation. Despite their fearsome appearance, they didn't kill other dinosaurs for meat, but they likely would have defended themselves well from predators. It is thought that the triceratops were herding animals and that they wandered the plains on all fours in large herds eating plants as they went. Sort of like buffalo or cows do today.

=== **MULTIPLE CHOICE** ===

9. **Your teacher asks you to locate the meaning of the word *brilliant*. Which two resources would be the most helpful?** (RI.5.7)

   A. A thesaurus and an encyclopedia

   B. A newspaper and a dictionary

   C. A dictionary and a thesaurus

   D. All of the above

10. **Your teacher asks you to find formation about the planet Jupiter. Which two resources would be the most helpful?** (RI.5.7, RI.5.9)

    A. A website about planets and a picture of Jupiter

    B. A website about stars and a dictionary

    C. A book about Jupiter and a world map

    D. A video about meteoroids and an encyclopedia

2.4. CHAPTER REVIEW

 prepaze

2. READING: INFORMATIONAL TEXT

11. **Your teacher asks you to find 3 facts about tornados. Which of the following resources would NOT be helpful?** (RI.5.7)

   A. A scientific report about tornados

   B. An opinion piece about tornados

   C. A news weather report about tornados

   D. A video of a real tornado

12. **You want to learn about sunburn prevention. Which two articles would be the most helpful?** (RI.5.7, RI.5.9)

   A. "How to Protect Your Skin" and "How the Sun Rotates"

   B. "The Best Beaches in California" and "How to Apply Sunscreen"

   C. "How to Apply Sunscreen" and "How to Protect Your Skin"

   D. None of the above

13. **You want to find out what you should feed your new pet turtle. Which of the following websites would NOT be helpful?** (RI.5.7)

   A. www.petfood.com   **B.** www.turtles.com

   C. www.turtlefacts.com   **D.** www.recipes.com

14. **You want to learn how to speak Chinese. Which two resources would be the most helpful?** (RI.5.7, RI.5.9)

   A. A Chinese dictionary and a translation website

   B. A Chinese dictionary and an article about Chinese food

   C. An article about China and an encyclopedia

   D. A translation website and a novel about a girl from China

---

➤ **Directions:** *Read the passage and answer the questions below.*

IN THEIR OWN CORNER OF THE ANTARCTIC, THESE PENGUINS ARE LIVING LIFE

Scientists were **alerted** to the penguins by satellite images, which are pictures taken from space. When they saw what looked like a huge penguin colony, they launched an **expedition.**

...continued next page

prepaze   **www.prepaze.com**

2. READING: INFORMATIONAL TEXT

Counting by hand and using overhead drone photography, they found 751,527 penguin pairs.

Looking at satellite images from as far back as 1959, researchers concluded that the colony has remained healthy over many years. Other colonies, such as the Adélie colonies west of the Antarctic, are in **decline**, as they are not as isolated from humans and are more deeply impacted by climate change.

Tom Hart, who works at the University of Oxford in England and is a scientist on the research team, said that searching for and counting the penguins was "**incredible**." He helped publish an important article about the penguin colony in the *Scientific Reports* journal.

2.4. CHAPTER REVIEW

=== MULTIPLE CHOICE ===

15. **What does the word *alerted* most likely mean?** (RI.5.4)

    A. Awakened
    C. Made aware of

    B. Scared of
    D. Overwhelmed

16. **What does the word *expedition* most likely mean?** (RI.5.4)

    A. Mission
    C. Announcement

    B. Explanation
    D. Advertisement

17. **What does the word *decline* most likely mean?** (RI.5.4)

    A. Refusal
    C. Reduction

    B. Unpopular
    D. Enlargement

18. **What does the word *incredible* most likely mean?** (RI.5.4)

    A. Unstoppable
    C. Underestimated

    B. Unpleasant
    D. Unbelievable

 prepaze

2. READING: INFORMATIONAL TEXT

> **Directions:** *Read the text and answer the questions below.*

THE DAY THAT CHANGED HISTORY

December 1st, 1995: A day that changed history. Rosa Parks, an African American seamstress at a department store in Montgomery, Alabama, was tired after a long day at work. She caught her regular bus and sat in the middle of the vehicle, towards the back. At that time, only white people were allowed to sit in the front, and if the bus was crowded, African-American were required to give up their seat to whites. Sure enough, more and more people boarded the bus, and soon there was no seating available for a white man who had just boarded. Rosa and several other African American passengers were ordered to give up their seats. Rosa refused, an act of rebellion that added fuel to the flame of the emerging African-American Civil Rights Movement.

Rosa was arrested that day, but her actions made her a heroine to many who were fighting the Jim Crow laws. Dr. Martin Luther King, Jr., a southern African-American minster, was inspired by Rosa's actions. He later became another famous activist in the Civil Rights Movement. Everyday working people were also inspired by Rosa. African-Americans in Montgomery decided to boycott, or refuse to ride, the public buses. Some of them had to walk over 20 miles to reach their destinations, but they kept the boycott going for over a year.

The boycott was more successful than they ever dreamed it would be. In 1956, the Jim Crow laws were abolished by the U.S. Supreme Court. The Montgomery buses became integrated, and the seats were given on a first-come, first-served basis. Rosa had succeeded in her resistance to segregation, and won an important battle in the fight against injustice. The Montgomery Bus Boycott was one of the first major protests in the Civil Rights Movement, but it was far from the last. Many more protests were made by the African American community and its supporters, but no one forgot the important contribution made by one stubborn woman.

2. READING: INFORMATIONAL TEXT

19. **How would you summarize the passage?** (RI.5.2)
   A. Rosa Parks was a seamstress who worked at a department store
   B. Rosa Parks refused to give up her seat on a bus to a white passenger
   C. Rosa Parks refused to give up her seat to a white passenger, which sparked the Montgomery Bus Boycott
   D. Dr. Martin Luther King, Jr. became a civil rights leader

20. **What does the text not explain?** (RI.5.1)
   A. Who Rosa Parks was
   B. Who Martin Luther King, Jr. was
   C. What the Montgomery Bus Boycott was
   D. What the Jim Crow laws were

21. **What is the relationship between Rosa Parks and Dr. Martin Luther King, Jr.?** (RI.5.3)
   A. Both refused to give up their seats to white passengers
   B. Parks inspired King as she did many other people
   C. Parks and King met at the department store
   D. Both were arrested on December 5, 1955

22. **What is one main idea of the text?** (RI.5.2)
   A. Rosa Parks' arrest led to the Montgomery Bus Boycott
   B. The Supreme Court made a landmark ruling
   C. Rosa Parks boarded a bus on December 1, 1955
   D. Jim Crow laws were segregation laws

23. **Which paragraph best describes the bus boycott?** (RI.5.1)
   A. Paragraph 1   B. Paragraph 2
   C. Paragraph 3   D. Paragraphs 1 and 3

2.4. CHAPTER REVIEW

prepaze

2. READING: INFORMATIONAL TEXT

24. What can you infer about Rosa Parks from the text? (RI.5.1)

    A. Rosa Parks did not have a family

    B. Rosa Parks was brave

    C. Rosa Parks was scared

    D. Rosa Parks needed to rest

25. What is a second main idea of the text? (RI.5.2)

    A. The Montgomery Bus Boycott led to a Supreme Court ruling that ended segregation laws

    B. Dr. Martin Luther King, Jr. was a young minister

    C. In November 1956, the Supreme Court issued a ruling

    D. Rosa Parks was arrested

26. Which line best describes the support for Rosa Parks' arrest? (RI.5.1)

    A. "Rosa and several other African American passengers were ordered to give up their seats."

    B. "Rosa was arrested that day, but her actions made her a heroine to many who were fighting the Jim Crow laws."

    C. "In 1956, the Jim Crow laws were abolished by the U.S. Supreme Court."

    D. "African-Americans in Montgomery decided to boycott, or refuse to ride, the public buses."

27. How did the event of Parks' arrest lead to the event of the U.S. Supreme Court ruling? Choose the best answer. (RI.5.3)

    A. After Parks' arrest, the Montgomery Bus Boycott began, which led to the U.S. Supreme Court ruling that integrated the buses

    B. After Parks' arrest, citizens walked 20 miles without riding the bus

    C. After Parks' arrest, the Montgomery Bus Boycott began

    D. After Parks' arrest, the U.S. Supreme Court ruled that bus segregation was illegal

2. 4. CHAPTER REVIEW

2. READING: INFORMATIONAL TEXT

28. **Which of the following is a key detail of the text?** (RI.5.2)

   A. "...no one forgot the important contribution made by one stubborn woman."

   B. "Rosa refused, an act of rebellion that added fuel to the flame of the emerging African-American Civil Rights Movement."

   C. "She caught her regular bus and sat in the middle of the vehicle, towards the back."

   D. "Sure enough, more and more people boarded the bus, and soon there was no seating available for a white man who had just boarded."

=================== **TRUE OR FALSE** ===================

29. **The reader can infer from the text that the Montgomery Bus Boycott was an important protest in history.** (RI.5.1)

   A. True   **B.** False

30. **Rosa Parks and Dr. Martin Luther King, Jr. were both significant figures in the Civil Rights Movement.** (RI.5.3)

   A. True   **B.** False

2. 4. CHAPTER REVIEW

prepaze

3. READING: FOUNDATIONAL SKILLS

3.1. PHONICS AND WORD RECOGNITION   **104**

- ❖ Letter-sound Correspondences and Syllabication Patterns
- ❖ Prose and Poetry
- ❖ Read with Accuracy to Support Comprehension

4.2. CHAPTER REVIEW   **110**

3. READING: FOUNDATIONAL SKILLS

～～ 3.1. Phonics and Word Recognition ～～

Common Core State Standards: CCSS.ELA-LITERACY.RF.5.3

Skills:

* Know and apply grade-level phonics and word analysis skills in decoding words.

> ➤ **Directions:** *Choose the best answer for the questions below.*

══════════════ **MULTIPLE CHOICE** ══════════════

1. **The root "vis" means see or look at. What does the word <u>revise</u> mean?** (RF.5.3)

   A. measure something once

   B. measure something again with a different tool or instrument

   C. look over something again to correct or improve it

   D. say something again to pronounce it more clearly

2. **Which word means "starting by itself; done without thought; routine"?** (RF.5.3)

   A. Elevation　　　B. Eject　　　C. Automatic　　　D. Retract

3. **What does the word <u>perspective</u> mean?** (RF.5.3)

   A. The way someone says something

   B. The way someone carries himself or herself

   C. The way someone looks at things

   D. The way something tastes

3. READING: FOUNDATIONAL SKILLS

4. **Which word means "normal; usual; regular; dull"?** (RF.5.3)

   A. Routine   **B.** Symbol   **C.** Decade   **D.** Ordinary

5. **The word <u>millimeter</u> contains the root "mille." What does the root "mille" mean?** (RF.5.3)

   A. One hundred   **B.** Measure   **C.** One thousand **D.** Less than one

6. **Which word means "one-of-a-kind; single; rare; special"?** (RF.5.3)

   A. Complex   **B.** Unique   **C.** Complicated   **D.** Analytical

---

➤ **Directions:** *Read the passage. Then choose the best answer for the questions below.*

GPS

At first, the military did not want to let civilians use GPS, fearing that smugglers, terrorists, or hostile forces would use it. Finally, bowing to pressure from the companies that built the equipment, The Defense Department made GPS available for non-military purposes, with some restrictions. On May 1, 2000, President Clinton lifted the <u>restrictions</u>, and announced that the option to <u>degrade</u> civil GPS signals during emergencies would be phased out by 2010. The federal government is committed to providing GPS technology for peaceful uses on a worldwide basis, free of charge.

7. **What does the word <u>restrictions</u> mean as used in the passage above?** (RF.5.3)

   A. Easily breakable   **B.** Make laws
   C. Enforce penalties   **D.** Set limits

8. **What does the word <u>degrade</u> mean as used in the passage above?** (RF.5.3)

   A. To reduce or lower   **B.** To increase
   C. To make more expensive **D.** To duplicate

 prepaze

3. READING: FOUNDATIONAL SKILLS

> **Directions:** *Read the passage. Then choose the best answer for the questions below.*

HONEYBEES

Honeybees live in beehives, which have a distinct order that helps things run smoothly. At the bottom of the totem pole are the workers. Workers are young female bees. Some of their main duties include going out to find food (nectar and pollen), building the hive, and keeping it clean. If necessary, Honeybees will travel up to eight miles to find nectar and pollen to bring back to the hive. Worker bees are actually the only bees that ever do any stinging. When this does happen, it is usually because they are trying to protect their hive from harm. A bee rarely stings when it is away from the hive, but it might sting if it senses danger. The lifespan of a worker bee is anywhere from four to nine months.

9. **Which word used in the text means "clearly different"?** (RF.5.3)

    A. Senses   **B.** Distinct   **C.** Nectar   **D.** Totem

10. **Which word used in the text means "to keep safe; defend"?** (RF.5.3)

    A. Stinging   **B.** Distinct   **C.** Lifespan   **D.** Protect

=== **TRUE OR FALSE** ===

> **Directions:** *Read the passage. Then answer the true/false questions below.*

THE FORBIDDEN BASEMENT

Jacob wanted to see what was in the basement, but he was <u>forbidden</u> to go down there without an adult. One afternoon when he was home alone, Jacob couldn't contain his curiosity any longer and snuck downstairs to the basement. Jacob opened a box and found a small toy inside. He began to crank a lever. Suddenly, a miniature clown <u>ejected</u> from the toy and startled Jacob.

prepaze   **www.prepaze.com**

3. READING: FOUNDATIONAL SKILLS

11. **The word <u>forbidden</u> means "not permitted; banned."** (RF.5.3)

    A. True   **B.** False

12. **The word <u>ejected</u> means "to have pushed something out with force."** (RF.5.3)

    A. True   **B.** False

> **Directions:** *Answer the true/false questions below.*

13. **The word <u>elevation</u> means "the circumference of a mountain."** (RF.5.3)

    A. True   **B.** False

14. **The word <u>seize</u> means "to let go of something slowly."** (RF.5.3)

    A. True   **B.** False

15. **The word <u>acre</u> means "a unit of area."** (RF.5.3)

    A. True   **B.** False

=== **FREE RESPONSE** ===

> **Directions:** *Read each sentence below and define the <u>underlined</u> word.*

16. **We had to be careful with her feelings because she was <u>sensitive</u>.** (RF.5.3)

    _____

    _____

    _____

    _____

    _____

3.1. PHONICS AND WORD RECOGNITION

3. READING: FOUNDATIONAL SKILLS

17. **There was an <u>obstacle</u> in the road that we had to drive around.** (RF.5.3)

_____

_____

_____

_____

_____

18. **The chair was an <u>antique</u> that had been in our family for years.** (RF.5.3)

_____

_____

_____

_____

_____

19. **The sunshine was <u>unexpected</u> because it was supposed to rain.** (RF.5.3)

_____

_____

_____

_____

_____

3. READING: FOUNDATIONAL SKILLS

20. I wanted an <u>apology</u> from him for hurting me. (RF.5.3)

_____

_____

_____

_____

_____

_____

3.2. CHAPTER REVIEW

prepaze

3. READING: FOUNDATIONAL SKILLS

3.2. Chapter Review

> **Directions:** *Read the passage and answer the questions below.*

SHINING A NEW LIGHT ON GROWING FOOD INDOORS

Mike Zelkind's farm is inside a large **warehouse**. The whole warehouse is bathed in purple light. It looks like a **futuristic** movie. But Zelkind's farm grows crops for the present.

Zelkind runs 80 Acres Farms, an indoor farm in Cincinnati. These farms are called **vertical** farms because the plants grow up and down instead of side by side in rows on the ground.

Plants have always relied on the sun for help with **photosynthesis.**

The farms like Zelkind's use **light-emitting** diode or LED lights. These lights look like a tube with two ends.

LED lights are changing how and when plants grow. The lights even change how long the foods last on the shelf and how they taste.

Zelkind's farm can change how food is made, priced and delivered in the United States.

MULTIPLE CHOICE

1. **The Greek root *photo* means "light." The word *synthesize* means "to form by combining parts." What is the meaning of the word *photosynthesis*?** (RF.5.3.A)

    Plants have always relied on the sun for help with <u>photosynthesis</u>.
    A. the process of using sunlight to make food
    B. the process of using lights to grow vegetables
    C. the process of making plants lighter
    D. the process of growing plants outside

3. READING: FOUNDATIONAL SKILLS

2. **The root word *mit* means "to send." What is the meaning of the phrase "light-emitting"?** (RF.5.3.A)

   The farms like Zelkind's use <u>light-emitting</u> diode or LED lights.

   A. transforming light   **B.** blocking light
   C. releasing light   **D.** wasting light

3. **Which of these letter combinations make an irregular sound in the word *futuristic*?** (RF.5.3.A)

   A. fu   **B.** tu   **C.** ri   **D.** st

4. **Which of these words has an irregular "air" sound spelling?** (RF.5.3.A)

   A. vertical   **B.** present
   C. futuristic   **D.** warehouse

5. **Which of these words has the same "al" sound as the word *vertical*?** (RF.5.3.A)

   A. principal   **B.** always
   C. calcium   **D.** male

> ➤ **Directions:** *Read the passage and answer the questions below.*

SHINING A NEW LIGHT ON GROWING FOOD INDOORS (cont.)

Zelkind agrees that some expectations are **unrealistic.** But he says his crops are fresh, raised without pesticides, and eaten locally. They use less land, water, and **fertilizers** than most farms. His **harvest** is not shipped across the country. Many farms have been hurt by **climate** change, but not his indoor farm.

LEDs allow fast, year-round growing. Zelkind and his team grow 200,000 pounds of **produce** and about 15 crops each year. They grow the plants in a warehouse that would take up about 80 acres on a normal farm.

Zelkind and 80 Acres President Tisha Livingston turned shipping containers and a warehouse into growing zones. They have systems that check everything the plants need. The plant roots are bathed in nutrient-rich water. Everything that comes from the plants is **recycled.**

3. READING: FOUNDATIONAL SKILLS

=== MULTIPLE CHOICE ===

6. **What is the syllable pattern in the word *climate*?** (RF.5.3.A)

    A. open   **B.** closed
    C. vowel team   **D.** r-controlled

7. **Which of these words has an r-controlled syllable pattern?** (RF.5.3.A)

    A. recycled   **B.** produce
    C. harvest   **D.** roots

8. **What is the best way to divide the word *fertilizer* into syllables?** (RF.5.3.A)

    A. fert + i + lizer   **B.** + rt + il + iz + er
    C. fer + til + ize + r   **D.** fer + ti + liz + er

> **Directions:** *Rewrite the sentence by correcting the prefix/sufix error in the underlined word.*

=== FREE RESPONSE ===

9. **She needs some <u>assistant</u> with her science project.** (RF.5.3.A, RF.5.3.C)

_____

_____

_____

10. **I purchased a new <u>unicycle</u> with three wheels.** (RF.5.3.A, RF.5.3.C)

_____

_____

_____

3. READING: FOUNDATIONAL SKILLS

11. **Walter was rewarded for his <u>leaderness</u> in the community.** (RF.5.3.A, RF.5.3.C)

_____

_____

_____

12. **The movie was <u>erupted</u> by a loud noise from the audience.** (RF.5.3.A, RF.5.3.C)

_____

_____

_____

13. **We took many <u>autographs</u> of the beach while on vacation.** (RF.5.3.A, RF.5.3.C)

_____

_____

_____

3.2. CHAPTER REVIEW

> **Directions:** _Read the poem and answer the questions below._

CASEY AT THE BAT

The outlook wasn't brilliant for the Mudville nine that day,
The score stood four to two, with but one inning more to play.
And then when Cooney died at first, and Barrows did the same,
A pall-like silence fell upon the patrons of the game.

A straggling few got up to go in deep despair.
The rest clung to that hope which springs eternal in the human breast.
They thought, "if only Casey could but get a whack at that.
We'd put up even money now, with Casey at the bat."

...continued next page

 prepaze

3. READING: FOUNDATIONAL SKILLS

> But Flynn preceded Casey, as did also Jimmy Blake;
> and the former was a hoodoo, while the latter was a cake.
> So upon that stricken multitude, grim melancholy sat;
> for there seemed but little chance of Casey getting to the bat.

MULTIPLE CHOICE

3.2. CHAPTER REVIEW

14. What is the rhyme scheme of the first four lines of this poem? (RF.5.4.B)

A. ABAB   **B.** AABB   **C.** AABA   **D.** ABCB

15. Which of the following expressions best describes how this poem should be read aloud? (RF.5.4.B)

A. gloomily   **B.** eerily
C. jokingly   **D.** mysteriously

16. Which of these words should be divided in the VC/CV syllable pattern? (RF.5.3.A)

A. preceded   **B.** stricken   **C.** former   **D.** also

17. Which of these words should be divided in the VCe syllable pattern? (RF.5.3.A)

A. was   **B.** springs   **C.** cake   **D.** deep

TRUE OR FALSE

18. A multisyllabic word is pronounced in one unit of sound. (RF.5.3.A)

A. True   **B.** False

19. It is important to emphasize a strict rhyme scheme when reading prose aloud. (RF.5.4.B)

A. True   **B.** False

3. READING: FOUNDATIONAL SKILLS

20. **The word hammock has a closed syllable pattern.** (RF.5.3.A)

    A. True   **B.** False

21. **The Greek root "dict" means "to say."** (RF.5.3.A)

    A. True   **B.** False

> **Directions:** *Circle the word that is used incorrectly in each sentence.*

22. **The mountain peeks were covered in snow.** (RF.5.4.C)

23. **I received many presences at my birthday party.** (RF.5.4.C)

24. **The gymnast won a gold meddle at the competition.** (RF.5.4.C)

25. **He is still deciding weather or not he will go camping tomorrow.** (RF.5.4.C)

> **Directions:** *Choose the word that best completes the sentence.*

=== **MULTIPLE CHOICE** ===

26. **When alternate lines rhyme in a poem (1 and 3, 2 and 4) this is called an _____ rhyme scheme.** (RF.5.4.B)

    A. ABAB   **B.** AABB   **C.** AABA   **D.** AABBA

27. **The Latin prefix _____ means "between."** (RF.5.3.A)

    A. poly-   **B.** pre-   **C.** super-   **D.** inter-

27. **The Greek suffix _____ means "the study of."** (RF.5.3.A)

    A. -ian   **B.** -logy   **C.** -ist   **D.** -ship

3.2. CHAPTER REVIEW

prepaze

3. READING: FOUNDATIONAL SKILLS

29. The word *fable* has a _____ **syllable pattern.** (RF.3.3.C)

   A. VCe   **B.** vowel team

   C. C + le   **D.** closed

30. The word *migrate* should be divided in the _____ **syllable pattern.** (RF.5.3.A)

   A. VC/CV   **B.** V/CV   **C.** VC/V   **D.** VV/CV

4. WRITING

4.1. TEXT TYPES AND PURPOSES   118
- ❖ Opinion Pieces
- ❖ Informative/Explanatory writing
- ❖ Narrative Writing

5.2. PRODUCTION AND DISTRIBUTION OF WRITING   126
- ❖ Clarity and Coherency in Writing
- ❖ Develop and Strengthen Writing

6.3. RESEARCH TO BUILD AND PRESENT KNOWLEDGE   133
- ❖ Build Knowledge Through Investigation
- ❖ Summarize or Paraphrase Information
- ❖ Draw Evidence from Literary or Informational Texts

7.4. CHAPTER REVIEW   142

4. WRITING

~~~~ 4.1. Text Types and Purposes ~~~~

Common Core State Standards: CCSS.ELA-LITERACY.W.5.1, CCSS.ELA-LITERACY.W.5.2, CCSS.ELA-LITERACY.W.5.3

Skills:

- Write opinion pieces on topics or texts, supporting a point of view with reasons and information.
- Write informative/explanatory texts to examine a topic and convey ideas and information clearly.
- Write narratives to develop real or imagined experiences or events using effective technique, descriptive details, and clear event sequences.

> **Directions:** *Read each passage and answer the questions that follow.*

ONLINE LEARNING PROGRAMS

Computers and technology are everywhere. These innovative devices have changed people's lives. People in all kinds of occupations - from students, to professionals, to homemakers - use technology to simplify their lives. In fact, even the way people learn has changed because of technology. Many people no longer attend school by actually going to class. The use of online learning programs is very common today. In my opinion, online learning programs are beneficial because it makes it easier for people to acquire degrees and there is greater flexibility about time and place.

People have hectic schedules that can make it hard to attend classes. Having access to online learning programs enables people

...continued next page

4. WRITING

to complete study programs at their convenience. This same flexibility makes it easier for learning institutions to provide students with more opportunities. In brief, a variety of courses and degree programs can be provided. With more choices for both the providers and the students, online learning programs can literally make our population smarter.

Undoubtedly, the availability of learning programs is relatively new, but given the surge in the availability of technology around the world, its popularity will continue growing in the future.

MULTIPLE CHOICE

1. **After reading the article, one can conclude all of the following EXCEPT:** (W.5.1 D)

   A. The author feels online learning is beneficial for learners who truly want to be prepared for future careers

   B. The author feels online learning allows learners more opportunities to cheat, by allowing someone else to do their work

   C. The author feels online learning allows learners to complete assignments and learn material without disrupting their daily schedules

   D. The author feels online learning is in the best interests of the learners

2. **The author states, "The use of online learning programs is very common today." Which of the following statements does NOT support this opinion?** (W.5.1 A)

   A. One in five students prefers attending traditional classes

   B. Approximately 50% of all college classes are offered online

   C. One in two college students has taken at least one online course

   D. All of the above.

4.1. TEXT TYPES AND PURPOSES

4. WRITING

3. **Fill in the blank.** (W.5.1 C)

    Online learning has become a more popular option in many fields of study. _____ several professionals have earned degrees without ever stepping foot into a classroom or gaining hands-on experiences related to their field.

    A. Specifically
    B. Consequently
    C. However
    D. Surprisingly

4. **What is the transition word or phrase used in the following sentence?** (W.5.1 C)

    "In brief, a variety of courses and degree programs can be provided."

    A. brief
    B. A variety of courses
    C. And
    D. Can be provided

5. **Which sentence clearly states the author's opinion of online learning?** (W.5.1 A)

    A. "Computers and technology are everywhere."
    B. "These innovative devices have changed people's lives."
    C. "Many people no longer attend school by actually going to class."
    D. "...it makes it easier for people to acquire degrees and there is greater flexibility about time and place."

6. **Which of the following could the author do to strengthen their argument?** (W.5.1 B)

    A. The author could provide more reasons to support their claim
    B. The author's claim could be supported by research
    C. The author could provide a counterclaim and rebuttal
    D. All of the above

7. **Which of the following statements is true about this passage?** (W.5.1 D)

    A. The author has not included a conclusion paragraph
    B. The author has not included a counterclaim and rebuttal
    C. The author has not engaged the audience by including a hook
    D. The author has not stated their opinion

4. WRITING

8. **Which of the following details from the article supports the author's statement that online learning programs increase lexibility?** (W.5.1 B)

   A. Students can study for a test while on their lunch break at work

   B. Students can register for classes to attend on campus at a variety of times

   C. Students can purchase textbooks to be used with the online courses

   D. None of the above

➢ **Directions:** *Read each question and choose the best answer.*

---

9. **A student is drafting an informational article about Sanibel Island's status as a barrier peninsula. Which of the following resources would be BEST to support the material being provided?** (W.5.2)

   A. A picture of the beach　　**B.** A map of Florida

   C. A diagram of the island　　**D.** None of the above

10. **A heading used in informational writing is MOST commonly found in which of the following locations:** (W.5.2)

    A. Before a body paragraph

    B. After the conclusion

    C. The middle of a body paragraph

    D. None of the above

11. **A student is drafting an informational article about Pluto's removal from the list of planets. Which of the following people would be the MOST appropriate to quote in the article?** (W.5.2)

    A. A Biologist　　**B.** An Astronomer

    C. A Teacher　　**D.** None of the above

12. **Which of the following should NOT be used in an informational article?** (W.5.2)

    A. Quotations　　**B.** Statistics　　**C.** Definitions　　**D.** Opinions

4. WRITING

13. **Read the following sentences. Which of the following transitions should be used to link the two sentences?** (W.5.2)

Christopher Columbus was a fifteenth-century explorer. John Smith was an eighteenth-century explorer.

A. By contrast   **B.** Even though   **C.** Nonetheless   **D.** For example

14. **Read the following sentences.Which of the following transitions should be used to link the two sentences?** (W.5.2)

Snow is one form of precipitation that falls during the winter. Sleet is frozen ice that may fall when the temperature is at or below freezing.

A. Contrast   **B.** Additionally   **C.** Nonetheless   **D.** For example

15. **If the author of a story introduces the main character as someone who is bubbly, giddy, and energetic, the reader can picture a person who is** _____. (W.5.3 A)

A. Fearful and quiet   **B.** Friendly and usually smiling
C. Angry and hateful   **D.** Worried and lonely

16. **Which of the following statements is MOST LIKELY NOT a narrative work?** (W.5.3)

A. Environmentalist Concerns Regarding Oil Drilling
B. The Little Puppy who was Lost in the Woods
C. The Angry Toy
D. A Lonely Adventure

17. **Which of the following details could NOT be used to develop a narrative about caring for a pet?** (W.5.3)

A. When choosing the best pet for your family, you must consider your schedule and how often you are away from home
B. Most pets need to visit the veterinarian several times within their first few months in order to receive all of their necessary vaccinations

...continued next page

4. WRITING

C. Most elementary students learn from taking responsibility for animals

D. Buttons was a tiny Pomeranian. He had beady black eyes and a soft tan coat

18. **Which of the following words or phrases can be used to show contrasting ideas?** (W.5.3)

A. The same way **B.** Similarly **C.** But **D.** Likewise

> ➤ **Directions:** *Read the passage and answer the questions that follow.*

EXCERPT FROM GODS AND HEROES

Zeus (Jupiter), the mighty divinity, overcame the Titans and became the master of the heavens and the earth. But notwithstanding his hard struggle, he would not have been victor had not Prometheus, the Titan, aided him. At last Zeus, ruler in the skies, became the enemy of Prometheus, who originated the hated race of the Titans, and only awaited an opportunity to punish him. He soon found the opportunity, for Prometheus was attached to mankind, whom Zeus intended to destroy, in order to people the earth with a race of older creation. Prometheus endeavored to dissuade him, but Zeus persisted in his purpose. Then Prometheus said: "Have you forgotten that the curse of the dethroned Cronus rests upon you and that by the decrees of destiny a mortal only can deliver you from that curse?" When Zeus heard this, he decided to spare the race of mortals. They were leading a wretched life and were unconscious of the spiritual or intellectual gifts conferred upon them by their creator. They knew not how to fell the trees and build houses to protect them against wind, rain, and the heat of the sun. Like the beasts, they lived in dens and caves which no ray of light penetrated. They knew none of the signs of the approach of the fruit-bringing Autumn, nor of Winter, nor blooming Spring. Destitute of purpose or perception, they lived like strangers in a barren world.

Prometheus pitied them. He explained to them the rising and setting of the stars and taught them how to recognize their orbits. He computed for them their numbers, a marvelous feat, gave them the power of recollection and the gift of writing, that highest of the sciences. He made the ox a useful servant to the race by placing

...continued next page

4.1. TEXT TYPES AND PURPOSES

4. WRITING

the yoke upon it and harnessing it to the cart. He bridled the wild horse and showed them how to use it for riding and drawing the wagon. They also learned from him how to build vessels and manage sails. He disclosed the depths of the earth to them with its treasures of iron, silver, and gold. Up to this time, men had no knowledge of plants or their healing qualities. Prometheus taught them how to avail themselves of this knowledge so as to relieve pain and cure disease. He also imparted to them a knowledge of what was transacted in the councils of the gods and taught them to observe the flight of the eagle. One element of comfortable living, however, was lacking for mankind. It was fire. Prometheus resolved to bring it to them from heaven, but the ruler of the skies ordered him to desist. Watching his opportunity, Prometheus soared aloft, approached the chariot of the sun, and stuck a rod which he carried in his hand in its blazing wheels. Then descending like a falling star, he brought to men the blessing of the fire. Hermes, the swift messenger of the gods, saw this and at once brought the news to the god father, Zeus. The all-powerful one wrathfully directed Hermes: "Up, hasten to Hephaestus (Vulcan) and say that the ruler of the gods needs his service." Vulcan, god of fire, was also god of all the artificers who are engaged with fire. He was honored as the discoverer of all the implements of the chase...

19. **How does the author describe the mortals?** (W.5.3 A)

   A. Silly creatures who loved to laugh and play

   B.   Intelligent creatures who knew how to make fire

   C. Powerful and courageous creatures, always fighting for good causes

   D. Uneducated creatures that lived like animals

4. WRITING

20. Put the following events in order according to the passage. (W.5.3 C)
1. Jupiter became master of the heavens and earth
2. Prometheus taught the mortals how to write
3. Prometheus tried to bring fire to the mortals
4. Zeus decided to spare the mortals

A. 1,2,3,4   **B.** 2,3,4,1   **C.** 1,3,4,2   **D.** 2,4,1,3

4.2. PRODUCTION AND DISTRIBUTION OF WRITING

prepaze

4. WRITING

~~ 4.2. Production and Distribution of Writing ~~

Common Core State Standards: CCSS.ELA-LITERACY.W.5.4, CCSS.ELA-LITERACY.W.5.5, CCSS.ELA-LITERACY.W.5.6

Skills:

- Produce clear and coherent writing in which the development and organization are appropriate to task, purpose, and audience.
- Develop and strengthen writing as needed by planning, revising, editing, rewriting, or trying a new approach.
- Use technology, including the Internet, to produce and publish writing and collaborate with others; demonstrate sufficient command of keyboarding skills.

> ➤ **Directions:** *Read the text and select the best answer choice.*

=== **MULTIPLE CHOICE** ===

1. **Which of these writing prompts best matches the text?** (W.5.4)

Recycling is a great way to protect the environment. It helps to eliminate waste and prevent pollution. Many people have the luxury of recycling from home. They can simply walk outside and place recyclable materials into the appropriate bin. This makes recycling extremely convenient. That is why our community should participate in this program.

    A. Write about something that you are proud of
    B. Write a story about a hero who saves the world
    C. Write a thank-you letter to your local garbage man
    D. Write a letter to your local waste management agency

prepaze

4. WRITING

2. **Which of these writing prompts best matches the text?** (W.5.4)

> I would like to express my appreciation for your attendance. I was so delighted to have you as a part of my special day! I had so much fun and I hope that you enjoyed yourself as well. See you next year!

A. Write a thank-you note to your favorite teacher
B. Write a thank-you note to your birthday party guests
C. Write about a time when you were a guest at a party
D. Write a complaint letter to a local party venue

3. **Which of these writing prompts best matches the text?** (W.5.4)

> Football is a very dangerous sport. Although the players wear protective equipment, this is not enough. I think that the entire sport should be banned. There have been countless injuries, some very serious and life-threatening. This has to be stopped immediately.

A. Write about your favorite sport
B. Write about the history of football
C. Write about your personal views on a professional sport
D. Write about a time when you won a game of sports

4. **Which of these writing prompts best matches the text?** (W.5.4)

> I am highly disappointed with our current lunch selections. I think that we should have healthier options. For example, we should eat vegetable pizza. This is a nutritious alternative to pepperoni or sausage pizza. Also, some students are vegetarians and do not eat meat. Vegetable pizza would be a good option for them.

A. Write a letter to your school cafeteria
B. Write a letter to a local pizzeria
C. Write about why you chose to become a vegetarian
D. Write about the ingredients needed to make a vegetarian pizza

 prepaze

4. WRITING

> **Directions:** *Read the passage and answer the questions below.*

How to Teach Microsoft Word to Kids
Use the Spelling and Grammar Checker

Step 1

Click "Spelling & Grammar" on the Review tab to launch the Microsoft Word spelling and grammar checker. Select the option to check spelling and grammar all at once.

Step 2

Select a suggested change for an incorrect word or phrase to demonstrate how Word updates the document. Again, explain the difference between "Change" and "Change All."

5. **Where can you find the Spelling and Grammar Checker in Microsoft Word?** (W.5.6)

   A. The Start Menu

   B. The Spelling and Grammar Checker box

   C. The Review tab

   D. None of the above

6. **Which of these tasks can you accomplish with the Spelling and Grammar Checker?** (W.5.6)

   A. Check your paper for spelling errors only

   B. Check your paper for grammatical errors only

   C. Check your paper for both spelling and grammar errors at once

   D. All of the above

4. WRITING

7. **Which of the following is true about the Spelling and Grammar Checker?** (W.5.6)

   A. This feature makes suggestions to help you correct spelling and grammar errors

   B. This feature will automatically make changes to spelling and grammar errors

   C. This feature is only for students who are bad at spelling

   D. This feature can be found under the "Home" tab

8. **Which of the following is NOT true about the Spelling and Grammar Checker?** (W.5.6)

   A. This feature makes updates to spelling and grammar errors in your document

   B. This feature can be helpful when writing a paper

   C. This feature can only change one error at a time

   D. The feature can detect errors in your document

=========== **TRUE OR FALSE** ===========

9. **Writing style may differ based on task, purpose, and audience.** (W.5.4)

   A. True   **B.** False

10. **It is best to start writing your paper as soon as you pick a topic.** (W.5.5)

    A. True   **B.** False

11. **Correcting misspelled words is an example of editing.** (W.5.5)

    A. True   **B.** False

12. **Kindle is an example of an E-book reader.** (W.5.6)

    A. True   **B.** False

13. **Dictionary.com is an example of an email address.** (W.5.5)

    A. True   **B.** False

4.2. PRODUCTION AND DISTRIBUTION OF WRITING

4. WRITING

> **Directions:** *Read the passage and answer the questions below.*

Mr. Schwarz is a great teacher. He motivates students to accomplish their learning goals. For instance, I was struggling in math class last semester. Mr. Schwarz assisted me with my homework and showed me some helpful math strategies. My friend, Dalia, needed help with a science project. She was quite frustrated. Mr. Schwarz showed Dalia a variety of volcano-building techniques. Her project was a success! These are just a few reasons why Mr. Schwarz is such an inspirational teacher. Mr. Schwarz was born in 1974 in Orlando, Florida.

=== MULTIPLE CHOICE ===

14. Which of the following is most likely true about the author of this text? (W.5.4)

    A. The text is a journal entry written by Mr. Schwarz

    B. The text was written for a scientific journal

    C. The text is an opinion piece written by a student

    D. The text is a school newspaper article written by a student

15. Which of these sentences needs editing? (W.5.5)

    A. Mr. Schwarz is a great teacher

    B. For instance, I was struggling in math class last semester

    C. friend, Dalia, needed help with a science project

    D. Her project was a success!

16. Which of these sentences should be removed from the text? (W.5.5)

    A. motivates students to accomplish their learning goals

    B. She was quite frustrated

    C. Mr. Schwarz showed Dalia a variety of volcano-building techniques

    D. Mr. Schwarz was born in 1974 in Orlando, Florida

4. WRITING

17. **Which of the following is most likely true about the technology used to create this text?** (W.5.6)

    A. This is a slideshow presentation created with PowerPoint

    B. This is a website from the Internet

    C. This is a document created with Microsoft Word

    D. This is a post created on a social media page

=== **FREE RESPONSE** ===

18. **Pretend that you are preparing to write an essay about France. List the steps that you would follow in order to search the Internet for information about France.** (W.5.6)

    _____

    _____

    _____

    _____

    _____

    _____

    _____

    _____

19. **List the steps for saving a document in Microsoft Word.** (W.5.6)

    _____

    _____

    _____

4.2. PRODUCTION AND DISTRIBUTION OF WRITING

4. WRITING

_____

_____

_____

_____

_____

20. **Give three examples of how to make revisions to a text.** (W.5.5)

_____

_____

_____

_____

_____

_____

_____

_____

_____

4.3. RESEARCH TO BUILD AND PRESENT KNOWLEDGE

4. WRITING

～ 4.3. Research to Build and Present Knowledge ～

Common Core State Standards: CCSS.ELA-LITERACY.W.5.7, CCSS.ELA-LITERACY.W.5.8, CCSS.ELA-LITERACY.W.5.9

Skills:

- Conduct short research projects that use several sources to build knowledge through investigation of different aspects of a topic.
- Recall relevant information from experiences or gather relevant information from print and digital sources; summarize or paraphrase information.
- Draw evidence from literary or informational texts to support analysis, reflection, and research.

> ➤ **Directions:** *Read the passage and answer the questions below.*

A SONG FOR HARLEM: 1928

Last November, Aunt Odessa, who was M'Dear's youngest sister, had come to Smyrna for Thanksgiving. She'd encouraged Lily Belle to apply for a place in the Harlem Young Writers Summer Workshop. "It's being sponsored by A'Lelia Walker," Aunt Odessa had explained. "She's the richest person in Harlem. A million-airess. Rich people impressed Aunt Odessa. She went on and on about how A'Lelia Walker had inherited her fortune from her mother, Madam C.J. Walker. "Honey, Madam C.J. Walker made loads of money from us colored women buying and selling her hair and skin products. She made us feel beautiful."

So Lily sent in ten poems that she had written.

"Nothing ventured, nothing gained," Aunt Odessa said. And she should know. She had moved to New York five years ago with little more than the clothes on her back.

Copyrighted Material prepaze

4. WRITING

═══════ **MULTIPLE CHOICE** ═══════

1. **How can this literary text be used for writing research?** (W.5.9)

    A. This is a science fiction novel and can be used when researching the genre

    B. This is a historical fiction novel and can be used when researching the time era

    C. This is a biography and can be used when researching the author

    D. This is an autobiography and can be used when researching the narrator

2. **Which of the following research topics can this resource be used for?** (W.5.9)

    A. Madame C.J. Walker

    B. A'Lelia Walker

    C. African-American millionaires from the 1920s era

    D. All of the above

3. **Which of the following resources would you most likely use, along with this book, if you were researching the Harlem Renaissance?** (W.5.7, W.5.9)

    A. A map of New York

    B. An illustration of Aunt Odessa from the book

    C. A history book about Harlem

    D. A tourist information guide about Harlem

4. **Which of the following would NOT be included in your bibliography entry?** (W.5.8)

    A. A Song for Harlem: 1928   **B.** Patricia McKissack

    C. Aunt Odessa   **D.** New York

4. WRITING

TRUE OR FALSE

5. **It is best to rewrite the entire article when taking notes.** (W.5.8)

    A. True   **B.** False

6. **Literary texts cannot be used for conducting research.** (W.5.9)

    A. True   **B.** False

7. **It is best to refer to multiple resources when conducting research.** (W.5.7)

    A. True   **B.** False

8. **A text can be summarized by restating the key points in your notes.** (W.5.8)

    A. True   **B.** False

9. **You could refer to an article by the American Dental Association when writing an essay about oral health.** (W.5.9)

    A. True   **B.** False

prepaze

4. WRITING

> ➤ **Directions:** Pretend that you are writing a research paper about the life cycle of a chicken. Look at the resources and answer the questions below.

chicken
life cycle stages

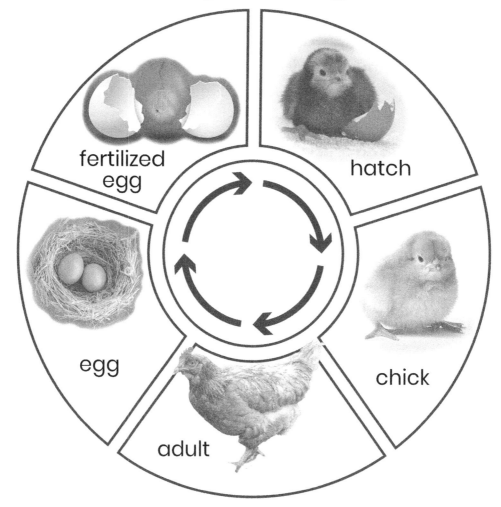

How a chicken changes and grows

prepaze

Copyrighted Material

www.prepaze.com

4. WRITING

A Brief Summary of the Interesting Life Cycle of a Chicken

First, the hen lays the egg. The baby chick matures inside the egg for approximately 21 days. The yolk inside the eggs provides the chick with much-needed nutrition as it develops. An important part of the process is when the hen sits on the eggs. She must sit on them to sustain a steady temperature and ensure that the eggs don't get too cold. She regularly turns the eggs over to make sure she is heating both sides evenly. After the incubation period, the chick emerges from the shell.

It then takes a further six months for the chicks to grow into adults. The female chicks become hens, while the male chick become roosters. Once they are fully grown, the chicks begin to mate and produce offspring of their own.

=== MULTIPLE CHOICE ===

10. **How can both of these resources be helpful when writing a research paper on the topic?** (W.5.7, W.5.9)
    A. Both the diagram and the article demonstrate the order of the life cycle
    B. Both the diagram and the article explain how long each cycle takes to complete
    C. Both the diagram and the article display pictures of each cycle
    D. The diagram and the article are not relevant to the topic

11. **Which of these sentences would you most likely include in your notes about hatching?** (W.5.8)
    A. "The yolk inside the eggs provides the chick with much-needed nutrition as it develops."
    B. "The baby chick matures inside the egg for approximately 21 days."
    C. "After the incubation period, the chick emerges from the shell."
    D. "She must sit on them to sustain a steady temperature and ensure that the eggs don't get too cold."

4.3. RESEARCH TO BUILD AND PRESENT KNOWLEDGE

4. WRITING

12. Which of these sentences best summarizes the text? (W.5.8)

A. Hens lay eggs and then sit on them to keep them warm

B. The chicken begins life as an egg and, after 6 months of development, becomes an adult

C. When they reach adulthood, the rooster and hen will mate and the life cycle continues

D. The chick inside the egg will grow for 21 days

13. Which of the following resources would also be helpful when researching this topic? (W.5.8)

A. A book about farmers

B. An article about egg nutrients

C. A photo of a male rooster

D. A video showing the life cycle of a real chicken

> **Directions:** *Pretend that you are writing an opinion piece about why students should be allowed to use cell phones at school. Read the article and answer the questions below.*

MORE SCHOOLS ARE ALLOWING PHONES, SO TEACHERS USE THEM FOR EDUCATION

Cellphones are still absent from most U.S. schools. Still, new data shows them steadily gaining approval. More school leaders are bowing to parents' wishes to keep tabs on their kids. Teachers are also finding ways to work them into lessons.

About six out of ten public schools did not allow cell phone use in 2015–2016. This was down from more than nine out of ten in 2009–2010. This is according to data from a survey by the National Center for Education Statistics. Among high schools, the shift over the same period was especially surprising. Schools prohibiting cellphones dropped from eight out of ten to around three out of ten.

The nation's largest school system, New York City, is among those that have abandoned rules against cell phones. Some students had been paying $1 a day to store phones in specialty trucks. These are

...continued next page

4. WRITING

parked nearby the schools. This was a promise Mayor Bill de Blasio made when he was running for office in 2015. He said this would help parents stay in touch with children.

FREE RESPONSE

14. **Pretend that you are taking notes for writing your essay. Write three points from the article that you would use to support your argument.** (W.5.9)

_____

_____

_____

_____

_____

15. **Explain how you selected key points of information from the article to write down.** (W.5.9)

_____

_____

_____

_____

_____

_____

4.3. RESEARCH TO BUILD AND PRESENT KNOWLEDGE

prepaze

4. WRITING

16. **Write a short opinion piece about the topic. Refer to the information that you gathered from the article as well as your own personal experience.** (W.5.8, W.5.9)

4.3. RESEARCH TO BUILD AND PRESENT KNOWLEDGE

_____

_____

_____

_____

_____

_____

_____

_____

_____

_____

_____

_____

_____

_____

_____

prep aze

www.prepaze.com

4. WRITING

> **Directions:** *Read the questions and select the best answer choice.*

===== MULTIPLE CHOICE =====

17. **If you were writing an opinion piece against skateboarding, which article would you most likely use to support your argument?** (W.5.9)

    A. Where to Buy Skateboards
    B. The Dangers of Skateboarding
    C. A Local Skateboard Shop is Going Out of Business
    D. The Inventor of Skateboards

18. **If you were writing a historical fiction story about John F. Kennedy, which book would you most likely use to develop your story?** (W.5.9)

    A. John F. Kennedy: A Memoir
    B. Great Speeches from John F. Kennedy
    C. The Life of John F. Kennedy
    D. All of the above

19. **If you were writing a research paper about ancient Egypt, which media source would you likely use?** (W.5.7)

    A. A TV show about a mummy
    B. A movie drama about Cleopatra
    C. A TV documentary about Egyptians hieroglyphs and symbols
    D. A video demonstrating a pyramid craft project

20. **If you were writing an explanatory essay about how to make lasagna, which article would you most likely use for research?** (W.5.7)

    A. The Top Three Best Lasagna Recipes
    B. Local Restaurant Wins Best Lasagna Award
    C. The Reasons Why I Dislike Lasagna
    D. The Origins of Lasagna

4.4. CHAPTER REVIEW

4.3. RESEARCH TO BUILD AND PRESENT KNOWLEDGE

4. WRITING

~~~~~ 4.4. Chapter Review ~~~~~

=== MULTIPLE CHOICE ===

1. **Read the following sentences. Which of the following transitions should be used to link the two sentences?** (W.5.2)

   Many states were undecided as to who they should support during the Civil War. Kentucky had soldiers fighting for both the Union a nd the Confederacy.

   A. Similarly   **B.** In addition   **C.** Meanwhile   **D.** For example

2. **Read the following sentences. Which of the following words should be used to complete the sentence?** (W.5.2)

   There are many precautions that can be taken to reduce the spread of disease, _____ effective handwashing.

   A. especially   **B.** meanwhile
   C. specifically   **D.** Both A and C are correct

3. **Read the following sentences. Which of the following words/phrases should be used to complete the sentence?** (W.5.2)

   Kentucky has four distinct climates; _____these are spring, summer, fall, and winter.

   A. Nonetheless   **B.** For example
   C. Specifically   **D.** Both A and B are correct.

4. **A student is writing an informational article about caring for a dog. Which of the following domain-specific words would MOST LIKELY NOT be used?** (W.5.2)

   A. Exercise   **B.** Nutrition   **C.** Veterinarian   **D.** Nocturnal

4. WRITING

> **Directions:** *Read the questions and select the best answer choice.*

5. **Which of these sentences would most likely appear in an opinion piece about music?** (W.5.4)
    A. "Jazz music became popular in the 1920s."
    B. "Country music is very festive and entertaining."
    C. "Classical music features a variety of instruments."
    D. "She hummed to herself as she listened to the orchestra."

6. **Which of these sentences would most likely appear in a newspaper article?** (W.5.4)
    A. "The Washington Bluebirds are expected to win the championship."
    B. "I think that baseball is the best sport in the world."
    C. "Catch the ball," yelled Tommy.
    D. "I've won lots of baseball championships."

7. **Which of these sentences would most likely appear in a letter to a politician?** (W.5.4)
    A. "Thomas Willett was the first appointed mayor of New York."
    B. "I would like to thank you for being an amazing friend."
    C. "Mr. Franklin, please consider making changes to the city's pet ordinance."
    D. "I voted for Mr. Franklin because I think that he is an outstanding leader."

8. **Which of these sentences would most likely appear in a recipe?** (W.5.4)
    A. "Don't forget to add the flour," said Monica.
    B. "Cane sugar is normally used for baking desserts."
    C. "Desserts can be very indulgent, but also quite unhealthy."
    D. "Once the water begins to boil, place the pasta into the pot."

 prepaze

4. WRITING

> **Directions:** *Read the passage and then answer the questions below.*

STOP THE SUGAR!

Donuts, potato chips, candy bars, and soda – these are just a few of the items that people dash into gas stations and convenience stores to purchase. People may have skipped lunch and are looking for a quick snack to get them through the afternoon. When they purchase these items because they are easily accessible and cheap, they are not purchasing snacks that will help them stay healthy. For this reason, I feel that sugary products should be taxed.

If people are forced to pay higher prices for their snacks, they might purchase healthier options. For example, if someone is asked to pay $1.50 plus tax for a bag of chips versus $1.50 with no tax for a fruit product, they might think twice about which item is best for them. All too often people choose snacks because they are making a quick decision. When people see that they are going to have to pay extra money, their thinking will likely change regarding which item to purchase.

Adding a tax to sugar products is another way to generate revenue for education and other public services. While some people might argue that this is unfair, it should be recognized that people are purchasing products they do not need. These sugary items are not necessities. They are wants. Taxing unnecessary items is a way to increase the state budget without punishing the population, since people can decide whether or not to buy these items. For this reason, I am in support of a tax on sugary products.

Choosing to tax sugary products is a positive step towards creating a healthier population. People are gaining more weight, and obesity is increasing at an alarming rate. When people are forced to pay more, they will hopefully choose healthier options. Some people may even learn that they like foods and drinks they have not previously tried after choosing new items instead of paying tax on sugary products.

Should a tax be passed on donuts, potato chips, candy bars, soda, and other sugary products? Yes! The decision to pass a tax on junk food will create more revenue for states, make people think twice about their snack choices, and aid people in consuming less empty calories. Let's take a stand to stop the sugar craze!

4. WRITING

MULTIPLE CHOICE

9. **According to the article, the author believes which of the following statements?** (W.5.1 A)

    A. Sugary foods should not be taxed because they are a necessity

    B. Sugary foods should be taxed because they are not a necessity

    C. If sugary foods were taxed, people would probably buy them anyway

    D. It is wrong to tax items people like to eat

10. **What is the main point of the second paragraph?** (W.5.1 A)

    A. Sugary snacks should be taken out of convenience stores and gas stations

    B. Sugary snacks are a quick and easy option for a healthy snack break in the middle of the day

    C. Sugary snacks prices should be raised allowing the stores to make better profits

    D. Sugary snacks should be taxed to encourage buyers to consider healthier snack options that are not taxed

11. **When an author asserts his or her opinion, they must do which of the following?** (W.5.1.A)

    A. Support their assertion with accurate, relevant research

    B. Create graphics sources that show the opposing side's viewpoint

    C. Ask questions that people who disagree might want to be answered

    D. Both A and B are correct

12. **Which of the following statements is false?** (W.5.1 B)

    A. Persuasive writing presents both sides equally

    B. Persuasive writing does not use research to support a claim

    C. Persuasive writing only uses direct quotations to develop a claim

    D. All of the above.

4. 4. CHAPTER REVIEW

4. WRITING

> **Directions:** *Read the passage and answer the questions below.*

1 Martin was exhausted from running in the sweltering heat. **2** He desperately needed relief. **3** As he entered the convenience store he stopped to enjoy the cool refreshing air.

4 "You look like you could use a nice bottle of water," said Mr. garcia. **5** He owned the store, and had recognized Martin as a regular customer. **6** Martin replied, "Yes, please. I am quite fatiged from the heat." **7** The store owner smiled and handed Martin an ice cold bottle of water. **8** Martin said, "Thank you. I have been back tomorrow."

=== **MULTIPLE CHOICE** ===

13. Which of these sentences contains a spelling error? (W.5.5)

   A. Sentence 1   **B.** Sentence 3
   C. Sentence 6   **D.** Sentence 8

14. Which of these sentences contains a punctuation error? (W.5.5)

   A. Sentence 2   **B.** Sentence 3
   C. Sentence 4   **D.** Sentence 5

15. Which of these sentences contains an error in tense? (W.5.5)

   A. Sentence 1   **B.** Sentence 5
   C. Sentence 6   **D.** Sentence 8

16. Which of these sentences contains a capitalization error? (W.5.5)

   A. Sentence 4   **B.** Sentence 5
   C. Sentence 6   **D.** Sentence 7

4. WRITING

> **Directions:** *Read the passages and answer the questions below*

PASSAGE 1

NELSON MANDELA

Nelson Mandela grew up with a different name. When he was a child, he was called "Rolihlahla." This name can mean two things: "pulling the branch of a tree" or "troublemaker." Some people did indeed think that Mandela was a troublemaker. He was passionate about the civil rights of the people, and didn't want people of different races to be segregated, or separated. Before he was elected president, he spent twenty-seven years in prison. The government sent him to prison because they didn't like his ideas and thought he might be dangerous.

Mandela was released from prison in 1990. Many people across the world thought it was unfair that he was in jail, and they protested his imprisonment. The protests were a big reason why he was released. In 1993, he won the Nobel Peace Prize. Mandela became the president of South Africa in 1994, a few years after he was released from prison. He was a well-loved president who kept the people of South Africa calm. He even stopped them from starting a civil war.

Nelson Mandela is known for being one of the greatest world leaders ever. He has many children and grandchildren to carry on his great legacy.

PASSAGE 2

NELSON MANDELA

Did you know that Nelson Mandela came from a royal family? He was the son of the chief of the Thembu tribe in the village of Mvezo in South Africa, where the villagers all spoke the language of Xhosa. Mandela was born on July 18, 1918, to chief Gadla Henry Mphakanyiswa (c. 1880-1928), and his third wife Nosekeni Fanny. The chief's four wives had four sons and nine daughters total. Mandela's father died in 1927, when Mandela was just nine years old. A high-ranking member of the tribe, Jongintaba Dalindyebo, adopted Mandela (known then as Rolihlahla) and taught him how to be a tribal leader.

 prepaze

4. WRITING

═══════ **MULTIPLE CHOICE** ═══════

17. **If you were writing a research paper about Nelson Mandela, which text would be the most helpful when looking for information about the meaning of his birth name?** (W.5.9)

    A. Passage 1
    C. None of the above

    B. Passage 2
    D. Both passages

18. **If you were writing a research paper about Nelson Mandela, which text would be the most helpful when looking for information about his parents?** (W.5.9)

    A. Passage 1
    C. None of the above

    B. Passage 2
    D. Both passages

19. **Which of the following is the best example of paraphrasing the text below?** (W.5.8)

    > He was the son of the chief of the Thembu tribe in the village of Mvezo in South Africa, where the villagers all spoke the language of Xhosa.

    A. He was born in Mvezo in South Africa, where the villagers spoke Xhosa.

    B. He lived with the Thembu tribe in South Africa. People in his village all spoke Xhosa.

    C. He was born in the Xhosa-speaking village of Mvezo, South Africa, and was the Thembu tribe's chief's son.

    D. He spoke Xhosa when he was little, and was the son of the chief of the Thembu tribe in the village of Mvezo in South Africa.

 www.prepaze.com

4. WRITING

20. Which of the following is NOT an example of paraphrasing? (W.5.8)

When he was a child, he was called "Rolihlahla." This name can mean two things: "pulling the branch of a tree" or "troublemaker."

A. The name, Rolihlahla, has two meanings: "pulling the branch of a tree" or "troublemaker."

B. In Xhosa, the name Rolihlahla has two meanings: "pulling the branch of a tree" or "troublemaker."

C. Mandela's birth name Rolihlahla has multiple meanings.

D. When he was a child, he was called "Rolihlahla." This name can mean two things: "pulling the branch of a tree" or "troublemaker."

> **Directions:** *Read the passage and then answer the questions below.*

4.4. CHAPTER REVIEW

THE LITTLE RED HEN

A Little Red Hen lived in a barnyard. She spent almost all of her time walking about the barnyard in her picketty-pecketty fashion, scratching everywhere for worms.

She dearly loved fat, delicious worms and felt they were absolutely necessary to the health of her children. As often as she found a worm she would call "Chuck-chuck-chuck!" to her chickies. When they were gathered about her, she would distribute choice morsels of her tid-bit. A busy little body was she!

A cat usually napped lazily in the barn door, not even bothering herself to scare the rat who ran here and there as he pleased. And as for the pig who lived in the sty – he did not care what happened so long as he could eat and grow fat.

One day the Little Red Hen found a seed. It was a wheat seed, but the Little Red Hen was so accustomed to bugs and worms that she supposed this to be some new and perhaps very delicious kind of meat. She bit it gently and found that it resembled a worm in no way whatsoever as to taste although because it was long and slender, a Little Red Hen might easily be fooled by its appearance.

...continued next page

prepaze

4. WRITING

Carrying it about, she made many inquiries as to what it might be. She found it was a wheat seed and that, if planted, it would grow up and when ripe it could be made into flour and then into bread.

When she discovered that, she knew it ought to be planted. She was so busy hunting food for herself and her family that, naturally, she thought she ought not to take time to plant it.

So she thought of the Pig, upon whom time must hang heavily, and of the Cat who had nothing to do, and of the great fat Rat with his idle hours, and she called loudly: "Who will plant the seed?"

But the Pig said, "Not I," and the Cat said, "Not I," and the Rat said, "Not I."

"Well, then," said the Little Red Hen, "I will."

And she did.

MULTIPLE CHOICE

21. **"Who will make the bread?" is an example of the use of**

_____ . (W.5.3 B)

   A. Transition words   **B.** Dialogue

   C. Descriptive words   **D.** Sequencing words

22. **Which of the following words can be used to signal the last event in a series of events?** (W.5.3 C)

   A. First   **B.** Next   **C.** Finally   **D.** Then

23. **What was the conclusion of this narrative?** (W.5.3 E)

   A. The Little Red Hen shared her bread with all of the animals

   B. The animals helped The Little Red Hen clean up and serve the bread

   C. The Little Red Hen refused to let anyone share her bread because no one would help with the work required to make it

   D. The Little Red Hen sold her bread to each of the animals

4. WRITING

24. **Which of the following would an author MOST LIKELY do at the end of a narrative work?** (W.5.3 D)

   A. Solve a mystery   **B.** Present a resolution to a problem
   C. Present falling action   **D.** All of the above

> **Directions:** *Read the passage and answer the questions below.*

How to Teach Microsoft Word to Kids
Create and Save a Document

Step 1

Open Microsoft Word by browsing the Start Menu. You can also show your student how to create a desktop shortcut or pin the application to the Taskbar or Start menu.

Step 2

Select the "Blank document" or another template on the Startup screen.Demonstrate how to browse for a student report in the Education category and also how to search for the template by entering "student" in the Search for online templates field.

Step 3

Type a report title on the file, and then save the document by clicking "Save As" on the File tab. Students can choose to save the file to their computer or Microsoft Live account.

Step 4

Encourage the student to save their work frequently to avoid losing it, should the computer or program crash. Demonstrate how they can set up Microsoft's AutoSaved feature. On the File tab, access Options, and select "Save." Select the "Save AutoRecover information every "X" minutes" and "Keep the last AutoSaved version if I close without saving" checkboxes. Microsoft recommends setting the AutoSaved function to no more than ten minutes.

4. 4. CHAPTER REVIEW

4. WRITING

FILL IN THE BLANK

25. **To open a document in Microsoft Word, you can browse the Start Menu or create a** _____. (W.5.6)

26. **The blank document template is located on the** _____ **screen.** (W.5.6)

27. **After you type in your** _____, **you should save your document.** (W.5.6)

28. **The** _____ **function periodically saves your work in case of a computer crash.** (W.5.6)

> ➤ **Directions:** *Read the questions and select the best answer choice.*

MULTIPLE CHOICE

29. **If you were preparing to write a research paper about dinosaur fossils, which of the following would be the best resource?** (W.5.7)
  A. A science fiction novel about dinosaurs
  B. A dictionary definition of the word *dinosaur*
  C. An article about a recent dinosaur fossil discovery
  D. A video about dinosaur eggs

30. **Which of these resources could you also use if you were researching dinosaur fossils?** (W.5.7)
  A. A local museum exhibit about dinosaur fossils
  B. A local library section with books about dinosaur fossils
  C. A TV documentary about dinosaur fossils
  D. All of the above

5. LANGUAGE

5.1. CONVENTIONS OF STANDARD ENGLISH   **154**

❖ Grammar and Usage

❖ Conjunctions, Prepositions, and Interjections

❖ Perfect Verb Tenses

❖ Capitalization, Punctuation, and Spelling

6.2. KNOWLEDGE OF LANGUAGE   **159**

❖ Expand, Combine, and Reduce Sentences

❖ Compare and Contrast the Varieties of English
    (e.g. dialects, registers)

5.3. VOCABULARY ACQUISITION AND   **166**
  USE

❖ Word Meanings

❖ Word Origins

❖ Reference Materials

❖ Figurative Language

                                                                                  173
6.4. CHAPTER REVIEW

5. LANGUAGE

~~~~ 5.1. Conventions of Standard English ~~~~

Common Core State Standards: CCSS.ELA-LITERACY.L.5.1, CCSS.ELA-LITERACY.L.5.2

Skills:
- Demonstrate command of the conventions of standard English grammar and usage when writing or speaking.
- Demonstrate command of the conventions of standard English capitalization, punctuation, and spelling when writing.

> ➤ **Directions:** *Read the question and select the best answer choice.*

=== **MULTIPLE CHOICE** ===

1. **What is the function of the underlined word?** (L.5.1.A)

    The frightened squirrel hid <u>behind</u> the bushes.

    A. This is an interjection used to show excitement
    B. This is a conjunction used to connect two clauses
    C. This is a preposition used to indicate a location
    D. This is a preposition used to indicate the time

2. **Which of these verb phrases best complete the sentence?** (L.5.1.B, L.5.1.C)

    John _____ in the choir since he was 9 years old.
    A. singing   **B.** has been singing
    C. will be singing   **D.** will sing

3. **Which of these verb phrases best complete the sentence?** (L.5.1.B, L.5.1.C)

    I _____ Mr. Johnson for a very long time.
    A. knowing   **B.** known
    C. have known   **D.** has known

5. LANGUAGE

4. **Which of these sentences contains an inappropriate shift in verb tense?** (L.5.1.D)

   A. He will be visiting us for the past two weeks.

   B. She has been teaching me how to swim all summer.

   C. The plant has grown several inches since we first planted it.

   D. My dad is sitting on the sofa right now.

5. **Which pair of correlative conjunctions best complete the sentence?** (L.5.1.E)

   You can _____ ride the train _____ take a taxicab.

   A. Whether; or   **B.** Either; or   **C.** Not; but   **D.** Rather; than

   ➤ **Directions:** *Use commas to correct the punctuation error(s) in each sentence. Write the correct answer in the space provided.*

   ═══════════ **FREE RESPONSE** ═══════════

6. **Use punctuation to separate the list items.** (L.5.2.A)

   The restaurant has locations in Phoenix Arizona Dallas Texas and Los Angeles California.

   _____

   _____

7. **Use a comma to separate the introductory word/phrase from the rest of the sentence.** (L.5.2.B)

   Afterwards he went home to take a nap.

   _____

   _____

5.1. CONVENTIONS OF STANDARD ENGLISH

prepaze

5. LANGUAGE

8. **Use a comma to set off an exclamatory word from the rest of the sentence.** (L.5.2.C)

   No I would not like ketchup on my hamburger.

   _____

   _____

=== **MULTIPLE CHOICE** ===

9. **Which of the following is the correct way to indicate the title?** (L.5.2.D)
   A. He wrote the article "The American Workforce."
   B. He wrote the article *The American Workforce.*
   C. He wrote the article **The American Workforce.**
   D. He wrote the article <u>The American Workforce</u>.

10. **What is the correct spelling of the underlined word?** (L.5.2.E)

    The sudden <u>avalanch</u> of snow nearly harmed the skiers.
    A. avilanch   B. avolanch   C. avalanche   D. avallanch

11. **What is the function of the underlined word?** (L.5.1.A)

    <u>Hooray</u>! We finally won the hockey tournament.

    A. This is a conjunction used to connect two words
    B. This is an interjection used to show excitement
    C. This is a preposition used to indicate a location
    D. This is an interjection used to show disappointment

12. **Which of these verb phrases best complete the sentence?** (L.5.1.B, L.5.1.C)

    I _____ dinner and washed the dishes last night.
    A. have cooked   B. will cook
    C. have been cooking   D. cooked

5. LANGUAGE

13. **Which of these verb phrases best complete the sentence?** (L.5.1.B, L.5.1.C)

Valerie _____ in that home for many years before she moved.

A. has been living　　　　　　　**B.** had been living
C. will be living　　　　　　　　**D.** living

14. **Which of these sentences contains an inappropriate shift in verb tense?** (L.5.1.D)

A. Jim is a very successful accountant
B. Mr. Rodriguez has been teaching for 40 years
C. Bianca has joined the basketball team next year
D. I would have passed the test if it wasn't so difficult

15. **Which pair of correlative conjunctions best complete the sentence?** (L.5.1.E)

_____ Suzy _____ Mario have seen the lost kitten.

A. Rather; than　　　　　　　　**B.** Whether; or
C. Neither; nor　　　　　　　　**D.** None of the above

> **Directions:** *Use commas to correct the punctuation error(s) in each sentence. Write the correct answer in the space provided.*

=== **FREE RESPONSE** ===

16. **Use punctuation to separate the list items.** (L.5.2.A)

The casserole recipe requires cheese broccoli chicken and rice.

_____

_____

_____

5.1. CONVENTIONS OF STANDARD ENGLISH

5. LANGUAGE

17. **Use a comma to separate the introductory word/phrase from the rest of the sentence.** (L.5.2.B)

As a matter of fact I think that Mr. Washington is quite a good teacher.

_____

_____

18. **Use a comma to set off the tag question from the rest of the sentence.** (L.5.2.C)

You would like to order a vanilla milkshake correct?

_____

_____

19. **Which of the following is the correct way to indicate the title?** (L.5.2.D)
   A. I am watching **Monster Attack**, my favorite scary movie.
   B. I am watching *Monster Attack*, my favorite scary movie.
   C. I am watching "Monster Attack," my favorite scary movie.
   D. I am watching *Monster Attack*, my favorite scary movie.

20. **What is the correct spelling of the underlined word?** (L.5.2.E)

You will be <u>compinsated</u> for your outstanding work.
   A. commpensated   **B.** compensated
   C. componsated   **D.** conpensated

5.2. KNOWLEDGE OF LANGUAGE

5. LANGUAGE

～～～ 5.2. Knowledge of Language ～～～

Common Core State Standards: CCSS.ELA-LITERACY.L.5.3

Skills:

* Use knowledge of language and its conventions when writing, speaking, reading, or listening.

=== FREE RESPONSE ===

1.   Combine these sentences to form one sentence. (L.5.3.A)

Michael has green eyes. Michael has brown hair.

_____

_____

2.   Combine these sentences to form one sentence. (L.5.3.A)

I ate a sandwich for lunch today. I ate an apple for lunch today. I ate carrots for lunch today.

_____

_____

_____

3.   Combine these sentences to form one sentence. (L.5.3.A)

Whales are mammals. Bears are mammals. Tigers are mammals.

_____

_____

_____

5. LANGUAGE

4. **Rewrite the sentence by removing unnecessary words/phrases.** (L.5.3.A)

Cindy's sister, Maggie, is her identical twin because identical means the same.

_____

_____

5. **Rewrite the sentence by removing unnecessary words/phrases.** (L.5.3.A)

The girl was crying because she was extremely sad, gloomy, unhappy and blue.

_____

_____

6. **Rewrite the sentence by removing unnecessary words/phrases.** (L.5.3.A)

It was so hot outside, we had to sit in the shade since it was hot.

_____

_____

> **Directions:** *Read the questions and select the best answer choice.*

═══════════ **MULTIPLE CHOICE** ═══════════

7. **Select the words that would best help to expand the sentence.** (L.5.3.A)

The _____ baby cried as I _____ soothed her.

A. Fussy; gently   **B.** Happy; harshly

C. Tiny; largely   **D.** Dirty; cleanly

5. LANGUAGE

8. **Select the words that would best help to expand the sentence.** (L.5.3.A)

The _____ wind shook the _____ tree.

A. Weak; sturdy
B. Smooth; jagged
C. Fierce; fragile
D. Steamy; cold

9. **Select the words that would best help to expand the sentence.** (L.5.3.A)

I walked _____ across the _____ bridge.

A. Warmly; Icy
B. Carefully; wobbly
C. Sadly; happy
D. None of the above

10. **Select the words that would best help to expand the sentence.** (L.5.3.A)

Lee gasped _____ as his guest yelled, "Surprise!"

A. With astonishment
B. shock
C. Excitedly
D. All of the above

> ➤ **Directions:** *Read the poems and answer the questions below.*

5.2. KNOWLEDGE OF LANGUAGE

POEM 1

The Blind Boy

O say, what is that thing called light,
Which I can ne'er enjoy?
What is the blessing of the sight?
O tell your poor blind boy!

You talk of wondrous things you see,
You say the sun shines bright;
I feel him warm, but how can he
Then make it day or night?

My day or night myself I make
Whene'er I sleep or play;
And could I ever keep awake
With me 'twere always day.

...continued next page

5. LANGUAGE

POEM 2
When I Was a Boy

Up in the attic where I slept
When I was a boy, a little boy,
In through the lattice the moonlight crept,
Bringing a tide of dreams that swept
Over the low, red trundle-bed,
Bathing the tangled curly head,
While moonbeams played at hide-and-seek
With the dimples on the sun-browned cheek –
When I was a boy, a little boy!

=== MULTIPLE CHOICE ===

11. **How does the language differ between these poems?** (L.5.3.B)
    A. Poem 1 is written in an older English dialect, while the language in Poem 2 is more modern
    B. Poem 2 is written in an uneducated English dialect, while the language in Poem 2 is more modern
    C. Poem 2 is written in English, while Poem 1 is written in another language
    D. Both poems are written in the same style of English

12. **What do these poems have in common?** (L.5.3.B)
    A. Both poems are written in modern English
    B. Both poems are written without a rhyme pattern
    C. Both poems are written from the first person point of view
    D. Both poems are written in a Spanish dialect

5. LANGUAGE

13. **Which of the following is the best example of English slang?** (L.5.3.B)

   A. In through the lattice the moonlight crept
   B. With me 'twere always day
   C. You say the sun shines brightly
   D. When I was a boy, a little boy!

14. **Which of the following is the best modern English version of this line?** (L.5.3.B)

   Which I can ne'er enjoy?

   A. Which I can ne'er enjoy?   **B.** Which I can near enjoy?
   C. Which I can enjoy?   **D.** Which I can never enjoy?

> **Directions:** *Read the passages and answer the questions below.*

PASSAGE 1

Elijah of Buxton

I busted through the gate, pulled Ma into the house, and slammed the door behind her. I was too worned out and shooked up to talk, so she started looking me up and down and spinnin' me 'round to try and figure what was wrong. After a second she said, "Lijah, sweetheart, you's scaring me to death! What's wrong, baby?"

Once my breathing caught up with me I let her know 'bout how the runaways from America had accidentally brung hoop snakes up to Buxton and how they were out in the woods rolling 'round looking for something to kill.

PASSAGE 2

Alice's Adventures in Wonderland

Alice opened the door and found that it led into a small passage, not much larger than a rat-hole. She knelt down and looked along the passage into the loveliest garden you ever saw. How she longed to get out of that dark hall and wander about among those beds of bright flowers, and those cool fountains; but she could not even get her head through the doorway.

...continued next page

5. LANGUAGE

"And even if my head would go through," thought poor Alice, "it would be of very little use without my shoulders. Oh, how I wish I could shut up like a telescope! I think I could, if I only knew how to begin."

For, you see, so many out-of-the-way things had happened lately that Alice had begun to think that very few things indeed were really impossible.

MULTIPLE CHOICE

15. **Which of the following best describes the language used in Passage 1?** (L.5.3.B)

    A. Slang   **B.** Formal

    C. French   **D.** None of the above

16. **Which of the following best describes the language used in Passage 2?** (L.5.3.B)

    A. Southern dialect   **B.** Slang

    C. Formal   **D.** Informal

17. **Which of the following best describes the dialogue register used in Passage 1?** (L.5.3.B)

    A. Professional and strict   **B.** Formal and fancy

    C. Casual and relaxed   **D.** All of the above

18. **Which of the following is true about these passages?** (L.5.3.B)

    A. The English style used in Passage 2 is more formal than Passage 1

    B. The English style used in Passage 1 is more formal than Passage 2

    C. The English style used in Passage 1 is the same as Passage 2

    D. The English style used in both passages is unclear

5. LANGUAGE

> **Directions:** *Read the sentence and write your response in the space provided.*

=== **FREE RESPONSE** ===

19. **Rewrite the sentence in a formal English style.**

Me and my pa went hikin' up the ol' muddy mountain.

_____

_____

_____

20. **Rewrite the sentence in a modern English style.**

O eagle, how does thou soareth so high in the sky?

_____

_____

_____

5.2. KNOWLEDGE OF LANGUAGE

5.3. VOCABULARY ACQUISITION AND USE

prepaze

5. LANGUAGE

~~~ 5.3. Vocabulary Acquisition and Use ~~~

Common Core State Standards: CCSS.ELA-LITERACY.L.5.4, CCSS.ELA-LITERACY.L.5.5

Skills:

- Determine or clarify the meaning of unknown and multiple-meaning words and phrases based on grade 5 reading and content, choosing flexibly from a range of strategies.
- Demonstrate an understanding of figurative language, word relationships, and nuances in word meanings.

> ➤ **Directions:** *Read the passage and answer the questions below.*

LITTLE WOMEN

Written by Louisa May Alcott

"Don't peck at one another, children. Don't you wish we had the money Papa lost when we were little, Jo? Dear me! How happy and good we'd be, if we had no worries!" said Meg, who could remember better times.

"You said the other day you thought we were **a deal** happier than the King children, for they were fighting and fretting all the time **in spite of** their money."

"So I did Beth. Well, I think we are. For though we do have to work, we make fun of ourselves, and are a pretty jolly set, as Jo would say."

"Jo does use such slang words!" observed Amy, with a reproving look at the long **figure** stretched on the rug. Jo immediately sat up, put her hands in her pockets, and began to whistle.

"Don't, Jo. It's so boyish!"

"That's why I do it."

"I **detest** rude, unladylike girls!"

       www.prepaze.com

5. LANGUAGE

=== MULTIPLE CHOICE ===

1. **Which answer best explains the meaning of the underlined phrase in the context of the passage?**(L.5.4.B)

   You said the other day you thought we were <u>a deal</u> happier than the King children.

   A. An agreement made by two people
   B. A large amount or by a lot
   C. The process of handing out cards to players in a game
   D. Joyful and free of trouble

2. **Which answer best describes the meaning of the underlined phrase?**
   (L.5.4.A)

   They were fighting and fretting all the time <u>in spite of</u> their money.

   A. The desire to hurt someone else
   B. To be offended or angry by an action
   C. Without being affected by something
   D. The ability to not care about something

3. **What is the meaning of the underlined word?**(L.5.5.A, L.5.5.B)

   "Jo does use such slang words!" observed Amy, with a reproving look at the long <u>figure</u> stretched on the rug.

   A. To calculate something using math
   B. A person's shape
   C. To notice or observe something
   D. A painting, picture, or drawing

4. **Which of the following is an <u>antonym</u> of the underlined word?** (L.5.5.C) "I <u>detest</u> rude, unladylike girls!"

   A. Hate   **B.** Amaze   **C.** Notice   **D.** Admire

5. LANGUAGE

> ➢ **Directions:** *Read the passage and answer the questions below.*

ALICE'S ADVENTURES IN WONDERLAND BY LEWIS CARROL

There was nothing so very **remarkable** in that; nor did Alice think it so very much out of the way to hear the Rabbit say to itself, 'Oh dear! Oh dear! I shall be late!' (when she thought it over afterwards, it occurred to her that she ought to have wondered at this, but at the time it all seemed quite natural); but when the Rabbit actually took a watch out of its waistcoat-pocket, and looked at it, and then hurried on, Alice started to her feet, for it flashed across her mind that she had never before seen a rabbit with either a waistcoat-pocket, or a watch to take out of it, and **burning with curiosity**, she ran across the field after it, and fortunately was just in time to see it pop down a large rabbit-hole under the hedge.

=== **MULTIPLE CHOICE** ===

5. **Which of the following is a <u>synonym</u> of the underlined word?** (L.5.5.C)

   There was nothing so very <u>remarkable</u> in that.

   A. Terrible   **B.** Unusual   **C.** Inspiring   **D.** Laughable

6. **Which sentence best restates the underlined phrase?** (L.5.5.A, L.5.5.B)

   ...it flashed across her mind that she had never before seen a rabbit with either a waistcoat-pocket, or a watch to take out of it, and <u>burning with curiosity</u>, she ran across the field after it...

   A. On fire
   B. Looking at her watch
   C. Tripping over her feet
   D. Eager to learn more

5. LANGUAGE

> **Directions:** *Read the passage and answer the questions below.*

ALICE'S ADVENTURES IN WONDERLAND

Suddenly she came upon a little three-legged table, all made of solid glass; there was nothing on it except a tiny golden key, and Alice's first thought was that it might belong to one of the doors of the hall; but, alas! either the locks were too large, or the key was too small, but at any rate it would not open any of them. However, on the second time round, she came upon a low curtain she had not noticed before, and behind it was a little door about fifteen inches high: she tried the little golden key in the lock, and to her great **delight** it fitted!

Alice opened the door and found that it led into a small **passage**, not much larger than a rat-hole: she knelt down and looked along the passage into the loveliest garden you ever saw. How she **longed** to get out of that dark hall, and wander about among those beds of bright flowers and those cool fountains, but she could not even get her head through the doorway…

=== **MULTIPLE CHOICE** ===

7. **What is most likely the meaning of the underlined word?** (L.5.4.A)

   <u>Suddenly</u> she came upon a little three-legged table, all made of solid glass…

   A. Confusingly **B.** Unexpectedly **C.** Gradually **D.** Bravely

8. **Which of the following is a synonym of the underlined word?** (L.5.5.C)

   She tried the little golden key in the lock, and to her great <u>delight</u> it fitted!

   A. Fury **B.** Surprise **C.** Pleasure **D.** Relief

5.3. VOCABULARY ACQUISITION AND USE

prepaze

5. LANGUAGE

9. The underlined word has multiple meanings. Which of these meanings best describes the word in the context of this sentence? (L.5.4.A, L.5.5.C)

Alice opened the door and found that it led into a small <u>passage</u>...

A. A piece of music **B.** A journey **C.** Part of a documents **D.** A corridor

10. What is most likely the meaning of the underlined word? (L.5.4.A)

How she <u>longed</u> to get out of that dark hall, and wander about among those beds of bright flowers and those cool fountains, but she could not even get her head through the doorway...

A. Had a strong wish or desire
B. Stretched out
C. Lasted a long time
D. Was scared of something

> **Directions:** *Read the sentence and answer the question below.*

════════════════ **FILL IN THE BLANK** ════════════════

11. Thomas learned a valuable lesson about <u>integrity</u>. (L.5.5.C)

The underlined word is a(n) _____ of the word *dishonesty*.

12. He felt a sense of <u>remorse</u> as he thought about what he'd done. (L.5.5.C)

The underlined word is a(n) _____ of the word *regret*.

13. He would finally reap the consequences of his <u>mischievousness</u>. (L.5.4.B)

The underlined _____ means "wrong."

prep⊙ze　　Copyrighted Material　　**www.prepaze.com**

5. LANGUAGE

═══════════════════ **MULTIPLE CHOICE** ═══════════════════

14. Which of the following best explains the root meaning of the underlined word? (L.5.4.B)

Singapore is a <u>multilingual</u> country. People speak English, Mandarin Chinese, Malay and Tamil.

A. The affix multi- means "many," and the word *lingual* means "pertaining to language"

B. The affix multi- means "often," and the word *lingual* means "pertaining to language"

C. The affix multi- means "many," and the word *lingual* means "lingering or long-lasting"

D. The affix multi- means "after," and the word *lingual* means "lingering or long-lasting"

15. Which of the underlined affixes means "beyond?" (L.5.4.B)

The movie is about a scient<u>ist</u> who <u>dis</u>covers a <u>super</u>natural force in an <u>inter</u>galactic world.

A. −ist   **B.** Dis-   **C.** Super-   **D.** Inter-

16. Which of the underlined words is a homograph? (L.5.5.C)

<u>Martha</u> tried to ease the <u>excruciating</u> pain with a cold <u>compress</u> and <u>aspirin</u>.

A. Martha   **B.** Excruciating   **C.** Compress   **D.** Aspirin

17. Which of the following best describes the underlined phrase? (L.5.5.A)

She wanted to go to the party but was she feeling a bit <u>under the weather</u>.

A. Metaphor   **B.** Simile

C. Personification   **D.** Idiom

5.3. VOCABULARY ACQUISITION AND USE

5. LANGUAGE

18. **What does the underlined phrase most likely mean?** (L.5.5.B)

He decided to be straightforward, rather than <u>beating around the bush</u>.

A. It means not to trim the hedges
B. It means to avoid telling facts directly
C. It means to give too many details
D. It means not to mistreat bushes

═══════════════ **TRUE OR FALSE** ═══════════════

19. **A word beginning with the affix inter- refers to something happening between two or more subjects.** (L.5.4.B)

A. True   **B.** False

20. **A glossary can be used to find the pronunciation of a word.** (L.5.4.C)

A. True   **B.** False

5.4. CHAPTER REVIEW

5. LANGUAGE

~ 5.4. Chapter Review ~

=== TRUE OR FALSE ===

1. **A homograph is a word that only has one meaning.** (L.5.5.C)

   A. True   **B.** False

2. **A metaphor is a figure of speech used to give objects human. abilities.** (L.5.5.C)

   A. True   **B.** False

➢ **Directions:** *Read the question and select the best answer choice.*

=== MULTIPLE CHOICE ===

3. **What is the function of the underlined word?** (L.5.1.A)

   The puppy was covered in black <u>and</u> white speckles.

   A. This is an interjection used to show anger
   B. This is a conjunction used to connect two clauses
   C. This is a conjunction used to connect two words
   D. This is a preposition used to indicate a direction

 prepaze

5. LANGUAGE

> **Directions:** *Look at the dictionary page and answer the questions below.*

5.4. CHAPTER REVIEW

1 progress

Middle English, from Anglo-French progrés, from Latin progressus advance

noun prog·ress\ 'prä-grəs, -ˌgres, US also and British usually 'prō-ˌgres \

1. a forward or onward movement (as to an objective or to a goal)

Synonyms: development, elaboration, evolution, expansion, growth

2 progress

verb pro·gress\ prə-'gres \

1. to move forward

Synonyms: advance, come, pace, proceed

═══ **MULTIPLE CHOICE** ═══

4. **Which of the following is NOT a synonym for the word *progress?*** (L.5.4.C, L.5.5.C)

   A. Development   **B.** Proceed   **C.** Regress   **D.** Expansion

5. **Which of the following NOT a meaning of the word *progress?*** (L.5.4.C)

   A. A decline in development   **B.** increase in growth
   C. move forward   **D.** advance towards a goal

6. **Which of the following CANNOT be found on this dictionary page?**
   (L.5.4.C)

   A. The pronunciation of the word *progress*
   B. The word *progress* used in a sentence
   C. The origin of the word *progress*
   D. Multiple meanings of the word *progress*

5. LANGUAGE

7. **The word *progress* is best described as a:** (L.5.5.C)

   A. Synonym   **B.** Antonym   **C.** Metaphor   **D.** Homograph

8. **Which of these verb phrases best complete the sentence?** (L.5.1.B, L.5.1.C)

   We _____ to Pennsylvania next summer.

   A. will be moving   **B.** have moved
   C. were moving   **D.** had been moving

9. **Which of the following titles should be underlined?** (L.5.2.D)

   A. A book title mentioned in a written essay

   B. A movie title typed in a document

   C. A poem title mentioned in an article

   D. A poem title mentioned in a written essay

> ➢ **Directions:** *Use commas to correct the punctuation error(s) in each sentence. Write the correct answer in the space provided.*

5.4. CHAPTER REVIEW

═══ **FREE RESPONSE** ═══

10. **Use punctuation to separate the list items.** (L.5.2.A)

    Lisa Janet Brenda and Molly were all invited to my sleepover.

    _____

    _____

11. **Use a comma to separate the introductory word/phrase from the rest of the sentence.** (L.5.2.B)

    For example alligators have wider snouts than crocodiles.

    _____

    _____

     prepaze

5. LANGUAGE

12. Correct the spelling error(s) in this sentence.(L.5.2.E)

Mr. Brown is an archaeologis at the local musuem.

_____

_____

13. Correct the spelling error(s) in this sentence.(L.5.2.E)

We atempted to locate the destenation, but we were unsuccesful.

_____

_____

> ➤ **Directions:** *Read the question and select the best answer choice.*

═══════════════ **MULTIPLE CHOICE** ═══════════════

14. What is the best way to correct the verb tense shift in this sentence?
(L.5.1.D)
She is jogging for several miles before she finally reached her
destina-tion.

  A. She will jog for several miles before she finally reached her destination

  B. She jogs for several miles before she finally reached her destination

  C. She had been jogging for several miles before she finally reached her destination

  D. She has jogged for several miles before she finally reached her destination

5. LANGUAGE

15. What is the best way to correct the verb tense shift in this sentence? (L.5.1.D)

He has written 5 articles by the end of this year.

A. He wrote 5 articles by the end of this year
B. He writes 5 articles by the end of this year
C. He will have written 5 articles by the end of this year
D. He have been writing 5 articles by the end of this year

16. What is the function of the underlined word? (L.5.1.A)

The movie started <u>at</u> noon, but we arrived late.

A. This is a preposition used to indicate the time
B. This is a conjunction used to connect two clauses
C. This is a conjunction used to connect two words
D. This is a preposition used to indicate position and space

17. What is the best way to correct the verb tense shift in this sentence? (L.5.1.D)

I am reading this magazine for the past fifteen minutes.

A. I have been reading this magazine for the past fifteen minutes
B. I has been reading this magazine for the past fifteen minutes
C. I will be reading this magazine for the past fifteen minutes
D. I will read this magazine for the past fifteen minutes

18. Which pair of correlative conjunctions best complete the sentence? (L.5.1.E)

I have traveled to _____ Costa Rica _____ Mexico.

A. not; but   **B.** both; and   **C.** whether; or   **D.** All of the above

19. Which pair of correlative conjunctions best complete the sentence? (L.5.1.E)

We will still go camping _____ it rains _____ not.

A. whether; or   **B.** rather; not   **C.** either; or   **D.** neither; nor

     prepaze

5. LANGUAGE

20. Which pair of correlative conjunctions best complete the sentence? (L.5.1.E)

She is _____ a singer _____ a dancer.

A. both; and

B. not only; but also

C. either; or

D. All of the above

> **Directions:** *Read the sentence and explain the literal meaning of the underlined phrase.*

═══════════ **FREE RESPONSE** ═══════════

21. I wanted to buy the television, but it costed <u>an arm and a leg</u>. (L.5.5.A, L.5.5.B)

_____

_____

_____

_____

_____

22. The soldier was as <u>courageous as a lion</u>. (L.5.5.A, L.5.5.B)

_____

_____

_____

_____

_____

_____

prepaze   Copyrighted Material   **www.prepaze.com**

5. LANGUAGE

> **Directions:** *Use commas to correct the punctuation error(s) in each sentence. Write the correct answer in the space provided.*

23. **Use a comma to set off the tag question from the rest of the sentence.** (L.5.2.C)

   The nighttime sky looks amazing doesn't it?

   _____

24. **Use a comma to indicate direct address in the sentence.** (L.5.2.C)

   Melissa I am extremely disappointed in you.

   _____

> **Directions:** *Read the sentence and explain the literal meaning of the underlined phrase.*

════════════════════ **FREE RESPONSE** ════════════════════

25. **The wonderful news was <u>music to my ears</u>.** (L.5.5.A, L.5.5.B)

   _____

   _____

   _____

26. **The <u>raindrops knocked on the window</u> during the tumultuous storm.** (L.5.5.A, L.5.5.B)

   _____

   _____

   _____

5. LANGUAGE

===== MULTIPLE CHOICE =====

27. Which of the following titles should be italicized? (L.5.2.D)

    A. The TV show Charlie the Clown

    B. The play Hamlet

    C. The book A Wrinkle in Time

    D. All of the above

===== TRUE OR FALSE =====

28. A thesaurus cannot be used to find antonyms of a word. (L.5.4.C, L.5.5.C)

    A. True   **B.** False

29. A word with the suffix sub- most likely refers to something underneath or below. (L.5.4.B)

    A. True   **B.** False

30. Which underlined word is misspelled? (L.5.2.E)

I can <u>assure</u> you that my <u>employees</u> are very <u>promp</u> and <u>reliable</u>.

    A. assure   **B.** employees

    C. promp   **D.** reliable

END OF YEAR ASSESSMENT

END OF YEAR ASSESSMENT

> **Directions:** *Read the passage and answer the questions below.*

WHAT SHOULD STUDENTS HAVE FOR LUNCH?

The Institute of Medicine is a group of scientists and health **experts**. It has pushed for healthier school meals. It recommends meals containing fewer calories, less fat and salt, and more fruit, vegetables and whole grains. Most parents would agree these are excellent goals.

A change in school lunch laws makes it easier for poor kids and foster kids to have school meals. It helps pay for their meals.

Still, there have been small problems. For instance, many high school athletes needed more protein than the **guidelines** allowed, so the government changed the rules.

Most school systems are working within the rules. Nine out of every ten now meet the new guidelines. Studies show most kids now like the new, healthier choices.

END OF YEAR ASSESSMENT

END OF YEAR ASSESSMENT

=== MULTIPLE CHOICE ===

1. **What does the word *experts* most likely mean?** (RI.5.4)

   A. Students   **B.** Specialists   **C.** Protestors   **D.** Supporters

=== WRITING PROMPT/FREE RESPONSE ===

2. **Write a problem/solution paragraph about the article. Write in the first person.** (RI.5.5, RI.5.6)

   _____

   _____

   _____

   _____

   _____

   _____

3. **Compare and contrast your paragraph with the original article in terms of structure, point of view, etc.** (RI.5.5, RI.5.6)

   _____

   _____

   _____

   _____

   _____

   _____

prepaze

END OF YEAR ASSESSMENT

> **Directions:** *Read the questions and select the best answer choice.*

―――――――――― **MULTIPLE CHOICE** ――――――――――

4. **Which type of technology would you most likely use to look up a keyword?** (W.5.6)

    A. Search engine   **B.** Email
    C. PowerPoint   **D.** Microsoft Word

> **Directions:** *Look at the outline and answer the questions below.*

Title: _____

Introduction: _____

Idea 1: _____

Idea 2: _____

Idea 3: _____

Conclusion: _____

―――――――――― **MULTIPLE CHOICE** ――――――――――

5. **If you were planning to write an opinion piece about electronic devices, which of the following would you most likely write on the "title" line of your outline?**(W.5.5)

    A. Read Books, Not Tablets
    B. Cell Phones were Invented in 1973
    C. The Story of the Magic Computer
    D. The History of Laptops

END OF YEAR ASSESSMENT

================= **TRUE OR FALSE** =================

6. **You could use a dictionary and a history website to write a research paper about word origins.** (W.5.7)

    A. True   **B.** False

7. **You could use a novel to write an opinion piece about its author.** (W.5.9)

    A. True   **B.** False

➢ **Directions:** *Read the question and select the best answer choice.*

================= **MULTIPLE CHOICE** =================

8. **What is the function of the underlined word?** (L.5.1.A)

    Fred was exhausted, <u>so</u> he decided to take a nap.

    A. This is a conjunction used to connect two words
    B. This is a conjunction used to connect two clauses
    C. This is a preposition used to indicate a location
    D. This is a preposition used to indicate the time

9. **Which of the following titles should appear in quotation marks?** (L.5.2.D)
    A. The book Anne of Green Gables
    B. The play Matilda
    C. The article How to Build a Snowman
    D. None of the above

10. **Which of these strategies are helpful when looking for unknown word meanings?** (L.5.4.A, L.5.4.B, L.5.4.C)
    A. Looking at context clues within the text
    B. Looking at word origins, roots and affixes
    C. Looking in a dictionary
    D. All of the above

END OF YEAR ASSESSMENT

END OF YEAR ASSESSMENT

> ➤ **Directions:** *Read the passage and answer the questions below.*

LITTLE WOMEN

Down they went, feeling a trifle **timid**, for they seldom went to parties, and informal as this little gathering was, it was an event to them. Mrs. Gardiner, a stately old lady, greeted them kindly and handed them over to the eldest of her six daughters. Meg knew Sallie and was at her ease very soon, but Jo, who didn't care much for girls or girlish gossip, stood about, with her back carefully against the wall, and felt as much out of place as a colt in a flower garden. Half a dozen jovial lads were talking about skates in another part of the room, and she longed to go and join them, for skating was one of the joys of her life. She telegraphed her wish to Meg, but the eyebrows went up so alarmingly that she dared not stir. No one came to talk to her, and one by one the group **dwindled** away till she was left alone.

=== **MULTIPLE CHOICE** ===

11. **Which of these dictionary definitions best describe the word *timid?***
    (L.5.4.C)

    A. Having a large amount of confidence

    B. Showing a lack of courage;shy

    C. Being upset about something

    D. A large gathering

12. **Which of these thesaurus lists best describe the word *dwindled?***
    (L.5.4.C, L.5.5.C)

    A. Shrank, diminished, ebbed   **B.** Increased, rose, expanded
    C. Chucked, giggled, grinned   **D.** Forgot, rejected, avoided

END OF YEAR ASSESSMENT

> **Directions:** *Read the poem and answer the questions below.*

PAUL REVERE'S RIDE

Listen, my children, and you shall hear
Of the midnight ride of Paul Revere,
On the eighteenth of April, in Seventy-Five;
Hardly a man is now alive
Who remembers that famous day and year.

He said to his friend, "If the British march
By land or sea from the town to-night,
Hang a lantern aloft in the belfry-arch
Of the North-Church-tower, as a signal-light, --
One if by land, and two if by sea;
And I on the opposite shore will be,
Ready to ride and spread the alarm
Through every Middlesex village and farm,
For the country-folk to be up and to arm."

Then he said "Good night!" and with muffled oar
Silently rowed to the Charlestown shore,
Just as the moon rose over the bay,
Where swinging wide at her mooring lay
The Somerset, British man-of-war;
A phantom ship, with each mast and spar
Across the moon, like a prison-bar,
And a huge black hulk, that was magnified
By its own reflection in the tide.

...continued next page

END OF YEAR ASSESSMENT

Meanwhile, his friend, through alley and street
Wanders and watches with eager ears,
Till in the silence around him he hears
The muster of men at the barrack door,
The sound of arms, and the tramp of feet,
And the measured tread of the grenadiers
Marching down to their boats on the shore.

TRUE OR FALSE

13. The main setting of the poem takes place in the present day. (RL.5.3)

    A. True   **B.** False

14. The poem is referring to a battle that is coming when it says, "Through every Middlesex village and farm, For the country-folk to be up and to arm." (RL.5.2)

    A. True   **B.** False

15. The theme of the poem is A Quest for Self-Discovery. (RL.5.2)

    A. True   **B.** False

16. The narrator of the poem is speaking to his friend. (RL.5.1)

    A. True   **B.** False

17. The main event happening in the poem is about ships coming in from England. (RL.5.3)

    A. True   **B.** False

18. Lanterns are used as a warning signal in the poem. (RL.5.3)

    A. True   **B.** False

END OF YEAR ASSESSMENT

> **Directions:** *Read the text and answer the questions below.*

TORNADO TRACKERS

Tornadoes are formed when a strong wind creates a funnel of circulating air. This rotating circle of air collects dirt, liquid, and dust particles in its wake and thus becomes visible to the human eye. The tornado funnel touches the ground and is connected to thunderstorm clouds in the air. The funnel is immensely strong and can trap cars, trucks, and even houses in its wake. It can circulate at speeds of over 200 miles per hour. If a tornado is approaching you, you must remain calm and find shelter as soon as possible. Go to the lowest point in your home, such as a basement or lower-floor bathroom. Make sure there are no windows in the room that could be broken by the tornado.

Not everyone tries to escape a tornado funnel. These are meteorologists who track and study volcanoes. These scientists often come dangerously close to the tornado funnels while doing their research.

But how do they learn anything from a fast-moving cloud of wind and debris? One important instrument that tornado trackers use is a tornado probe. Resembling a small orange construction cone, this vital piece of equipment contains sensors that record and track temperature, pressure, wind speed, and direction inside the funnel. Sometimes the probe can even film what's happening inside the tornado.

Scientists track tornadoes through measurements of wind speed and pressure in an area. They also watch weather reports to estimate the possible location of a tornado. Sometimes their calculations are off, and they miss the tornado completely and have

...continued next page

 prepaze

END OF YEAR ASSESSMENT

to try another location close by.

When they locate a tornado, the scientists place the probe where they think the funnel will be. Then they hope for the best. If the funnel goes over the probe, the scientists can use its measurements to make their future predictions of tornado patterns more accurate.

Tornado trackers are some of the bravest people around. They risk their lives to help others avoid these dangerous natural disasters.

══ TRUE OR FALSE ══

19. **A main idea of the text is that tornado trackers use instruments to get information to help them warn people about tornadoes.** (RI.5.2)

     A. True   **B.** False

20. **A tornado probe is yellow and square shaped.** (RI.5.1)

     A. True   **B.** False

21. **Scientists use tornado probes to predict future tornados.** (RI.5.3)

     A. True   **B.** False

22. **The tornado scientists are called "wind catchers."** (RI.5.3)

     A. True   **B.** False

23. **The reader can infer that this text is about the massive destruction of tornadoes.** (RI.5.1)

     A. True   **B.** False

24. **The line: "...this vital piece of equipment contains sensors that record and track temperature, pressure, wind speed, and direction inside the funnel." is a key detail that supports why tornado probes are important tools used by tornado scientists.** (RI.5.2)

     A. True   **B.** False

END OF YEAR ASSESSMENT

> **Directions**:*Read the passage and answer the questions.*

FIFTY FAMOUS PEOPLE

One day King Henry the Fourth of France was hunting in a large forest. Towards evening he told his men to ride home by the main road while he went by another way that was somewhat longer.

As he came out of the forest he saw a little boy by the roadside, who seemed to be watching for someone.

"Well, my boy," said the king, "are you looking for your father?"

"No, sir," answered the boy. "I am looking for the king. They say he is hunting in the woods, and perhaps will ride out this way. So I'm waiting to see him."

"Oh, if that is what you wish," said King Henry, "get up behind me on the horse and I'll take you to the place where you will see him."

The boy got up at once, and sat behind the king. The horse cantered briskly along, and king and boy were soon quite well acquainted.

"They say that King Henry always has a number of men with him," said the boy, "how shall I know which is he?"

"Oh, that will be easy enough," was the answer. "All the other men will take off their hats, but the king will keep his on."

"Do you mean that the one with his hat on will be the king?"

"Certainly."

Soon they came into the main road where a number of the king's men were waiting. All the men seemed amused when they saw the boy, and as they rode up, they greeted the king by taking off their hats.

"Well, my boy," said King Henry, "which do you think is the king?"

"I don't know," answered the boy; "but it must be either you or I, for we both have our hats on."

 prepaze

END OF YEAR ASSESSMENT

END OF YEAR ASSESSMENT

═══════════════ **MULTIPLE CHOICE** ═══════════════

25. The author included the king's explanation about the hats for what reason? (RL5.5)

   A. To detail the king's important wardrobe
   B. To describe the different hats the king wears
   C. To show who is the king
   D. To explain what the king's hat will look like

26. The boy answered that "but it must be either you or I, for we both have our hats on." Why was this line included at the end of the story? (RL5.5)

   A. He isn't sure if he is riding with the king
   B. He definitely knows who the king is
   C. He is surprised that he was riding with the king all along
   D. He still doesn't know who the king is

27. When "the horse cantered briskly along," this means what? (RL5.4)

   A. To move to the edge   **B.** To walk slowly
   C. To make noise loudly   **D.** To gallop quickly

═══════════════ **FREE FORM RESPONSE** ═══════════════

28. How do you know that the narrator's viewpoint of the king is that of someone who is compassionate towards children? (RL5.6)

_____

_____

_____

_____

_____

prepaze   **www.prepaze.com**

END OF YEAR ASSESSMENT

> **Directions**:*Read the passage and answer the questions.*

FIFTY FAMOUS PEOPLE

An old Cat was in a fair way to kill all the Mice in the barn.

One day the Mice met to talk about the great harm that she was doing them. Each one told of some plan by which to keep out of her way.

"Do as I say," said an old gray Mouse that was thought to be very wise."Do as I say. Hang a bell to the Cat's neck. Then, when we hear it ring, we shall know that she is coming, and can scamper out of her way.""Good! Good!" said all the other Mice; and one ran to get the bell. "Now which of you will hang this bell on the Cat's neck?" said the old gray Mouse.

"Not! Not!" said all the mice together. And they scampered away to their holes.

════════ **MULTIPLE CHOICE** ════════

29. **How did the line below influence the rest of the story?** (RL5.5)

    "An old Cat was in a fair way to kill all the Mice in the barn."

    A. It sets the scene for the rest of the story
       It describes the main characters in the story
    B. It explains the relationships between the characters
    C. It describes the main problem in the story

30. **At the end of the story, none of the mice will hang the bell around the Cat's neck. What does this reveal about the narrator's viewpoint of the Mice?** (RL5.6)

    A. The mice are the villains   **B.** The mice are smart
    C. The mice are brave   **D.** The mice are scared

     prepaze

END OF YEAR ASSESSMENT

> ➤ **Directions:** *Read the passage and answer the questions below.*

The Tale of Johnny Town-Mouse

Johnny Town-mouse was born in a cupboard. Timmy Willie was born in a garden. Timmy Willie was a little country mouse who went to town by mistake in a hamper. The gardener sent vegetables to town once a week by the carrier; he packed them in a big hamper.

The gardener left the hamper by the garden gate, so that the carrier could pick it up when he passed. Timmy Willie crept in through a hole in the wickerwork, and after eating some peas—Timmy Willie fell fast asleep.

He awoke in a fright, while the hamper was being lifted into the carrier's cart. Then there was a jolting, and a clattering of horse's feet; other packages were thrown in; for miles and miles—jolt—jolt—jolt! and Timmy Willie trembled amongst the jumbled-up vegetables.

At last, the cart stopped at a house, where the hamper was taken out, carried in, and set down. The cook gave the carrier sixpence; the back door banged, and the cart rumbled away. But there was no quiet; there seemed to be hundreds of carts passing. Dogs barked; boys whistled in the street; the cook laughed, the parlor maid ran up and down-stairs; and a canary sang like a steam engine.

Timmy Willie, who had lived all his life in a garden, was almost frightened to death. Presently the cook opened the hamper and began to unpack the vegetables. Out sprang the terrified Timmy Willie.

Up jumped the cook on a chair, exclaiming "A mouse! a mouse! Call the cat! Fetch me the poker, Sarah!" Timmy Willie did not wait for Sarah with the poker; he rushed along the skirting board till he came to a little hole, and in he popped.

He dropped half a foot, and crashed into the middle of a mouse dinner party, breaking three glasses.—"Who in the world is this?" inquired Johnny Town-mouse. But after the first exclamation of surprise, he instantly recovered his manners.

With the utmost politeness, he introduced Timmy Willie to nine other mice, all with long tails and white neckties. Timmy Willie's own tail was insignificant. Johnny Town-mouse and his friends noticed it; but they were too well-bred to make personal remarks; only one of them asked Timmy Willie if he had ever been in a trap.

...continued next page

END OF YEAR ASSESSMENT

The dinner was of eight courses; not much of anything, but truly elegant. All the dishes were unknown to Timmy Willie, who would have been a little afraid of tasting them; only he was very hungry and very anxious to behave with company manners. The continual noise upstairs made him so nervous, that he dropped a plate. "Never mind, they don't belong to us," said Johnny.

"Why don't those youngsters come back with the dessert?" It should be explained that two young mice, who were waiting on the others, went skirmishing upstairs to the kitchen between courses. Several times they had come tumbling in, squeaking and laughing; Timmy Willie learned with horror that they were being chased by the cat. His appetite failed, he felt faint. "Try some jelly?" said Johnny Town-mouse.

"No? Would you rather go to bed? I will show you a most comfortable sofa pillow."

The sofa pillow had a hole in it. Johnny Town-mouse quite honestly recommended it as the best bed, kept exclusively for visitors. But the sofa smelled of cat. Timmy Willie preferred to spend a miserable night under the fender.

It was just the same next day. An excellent breakfast was provided—for mice accustomed to eating bacon; but Timmy Willie had been reared on roots and salad. Johnny Town-mouse and his friends racketed about under the floors and came boldly out all over the house in the evening. One particularly loud crash had been caused by Sarah tumbling downstairs with the tea-tray; there were crumbs and sugar and smears of jam to be collected, in spite of the cat.

Timmy Willie longed to be at home in his peaceful nest in a sunny bank. The food disagreed with him; the noise prevented him from sleeping. In a few days, he grew so thin that Johnny Town-mouse noticed it and questioned him. He listened to Timmy Willie's story and inquired about the garden. "It sounds rather a dull place. What do you do when it rains?"

"When it rains, I sit in my little sandy burrow and shell corn and seeds from my Autumn store. I peep out at the throstles and blackbirds on the lawn, and my friend Cock Robin. And when the sun comes out again, you should see my garden and the flowers—roses and pinks and pansies—no noise except the birds and bees, and the lambs in the meadows."

...continued next page

 prepaze

END OF YEAR ASSESSMENT

"There goes that cat again!" exclaimed Johnny Town-mouse. When they had taken refuge in the coal-cellar he resumed the conversation; "I confess I am a little disappointed; we have endeavored to entertain you, Timothy William."

"Oh yes, yes, you have been most kind; but I do feel so ill," said Timmy Willie.

"It may be that your teeth and digestion are unaccustomed to our food; perhaps it might be wiser for you to return in the hamper."

"Oh? Oh!" cried Timmy Willie.

"Why of course for the matter of that we could have sent you back last week," said Johnny rather huffily—"did you not know that the hamper goes back empty on Saturdays?"

So, Timmy Willie said good-bye to his new friends, and hid in the hamper with a crumb of cake and a withered cabbage leaf; and after much jolting, he was set down safely in his own garden.

31. "At last, the cart stopped at a house, where the hamper was taken out, carried in, and set down. The cook gave the carrier sixpence; the back door banged, and the cart rumbled away. But there was no quiet; there seemed to be hundreds of carts passing. Dogs barked; boys whistled in the street; the cook laughed, the parlor maid ran up and down-stairs; and a canary sang like a steam engine."

How would this portion of the passage be different if it were part of a video? (RL.5.7)

A. Instead of hearing a description of sounds, the viewer would hear the sounds

B. It would be read aloud instead of typed out

C. It would not be as descriptive

D. It would not include as much detail

END OF YEAR ASSESSMENT

> **Directions:** *Read the passages and answer the questions below.*

HOW TO BUILD A KITE

You can purchase a kite from your local toy store, but it is much more exciting to construct your own. The instructions for building a kite are quite simple. First, you will need sticks or wooden dowels. Place your sticks in the shape of a cross, and fasten it with a string. Next, use a light material, such as a newspaper or a large plastic bag, to make your kite sail. You may need to cut the sail so that it properly fits the stick frame. Attach and secure your sail over the frame with glue. Lastly, tie a long string to the intersection of the frame.

WHEN CAN I FLY MY KITE?

Wind is very important when it comes to flying a kite. It is very difficult to fly a kite without the perfect breeze. Wind speeds between 5-15 miles per hour are strong enough to propel your kite. You should avoid excessively strong winds which can destroy the frame and sail. Also, do not fly a kite during a thunderstorm. Warm, windy days are the best for kite flying.

═══════════════ **MULTIPLE CHOICE** ═══════════════

32. How do both of these passages help to develop the topic? (RI.5.7, RI.5.9)

 A. The reader can learn various information about kites

 B. The reader can learn how to enter a kite flying contest

 C. The reader can locate a store that sells kites nearby

 D. None of the above

33. Which of the following texts would best help to develop the topic?
(RI.5.7, RI.5.9)

 A. An article about the history of kites

 B. An article about windstorms

 C. An article about kite flying techniques

 D. An article about the inventor of the first kite

Copyrighted Material prepaze

END OF YEAR ASSESSMENT

34. **Which of the following resources would NOT be relevant to the topic?** (RI.5.7, RI.5.9)
    A. A kite pattern book
    B. A dictionary definition of the word *kite*
    C. A video of someone making a kite
    D. An article written by a professional kite maker

> **Directions:** *Look at the chart and read the passage. Then answer the questions below.*

Body of Water	Description
River	a large body of water that flows in one direction
Lake	a large body of standing (or slow-moving) water that is surrounded by land
Ocean	a large body of water with no visible boundaries
Gulf	a large area (partially surrounded by land) into which water from the ocean flows and collects

DIFFERENT BODIES OF WATER, EXPLAINED

Did you know that 96 percent of water from the Earth comes from the ocean? However, people don't drink ocean water– it's far too salty! Water used for drinking and bathing comes from freshwater reservoirs like rivers and lakes. Bodies of water are classified, or categorized, in a few different ways.

A river is a fairly large, quick-moving body of water that always moves in the same direction. A river's depth can swell or shrink depending on the amount of rain that falls. Sometimes a river will flow

...continued next page

END OF YEAR ASSESSMENT

into another body of water called a lake.

A lake is a body of water that is surrounded by land on all sides. It is not as fast-moving as a river- in fact, sometimes the water doesn't move at all! Water mostly flows into a lake from rivers, melting ice snow, and precipitation such as rain.

An ocean is the largest body of water that exists. Oceans do not contain fresh water like lakes and rivers do. Instead, they are made up of salt water. When you look at an ocean from the coast, you cannot see where it ends. A gulf is also made up of sea water. It is an area of water in the ocean that is surrounded on three sides by land. Water in a gulf has fewer currents than the open ocean. Smaller gulfs in the ocean are called coves or bays.

=== **MULTIPLE CHOICE** ===

35. **Which of the following is true about these texts?** (RI.5.7, RI.5.9)

   A. The chart organizes and simplifies the information from the passage

   B. The passage further explains the details from the chart

   C. The chart and the passage can both help to develop the topic

   D. All of the above

> **Directions:** *Read the passage. Then answer the questions below.*

STOP THE SUGAR!

Donuts, potato chips, candy bars, and soda – these are just a few of the items that people dash into gas stations and convenience stores to purchase. People may have skipped lunch or are looking for a quick snack to get them through the afternoon. When they purchase these items because they are easily accessible and cheap, they are not purchasing snacks that will help them stay healthy. For this reason, I feel that sugary products should be taxed.

If people are forced to pay higher prices for their snacks, they might purchase healthier options. For example, if someone is asked to pay $1.50 plus tax for a bag of chips versus $1.50 with no tax for a

...continued next page

END OF YEAR ASSESSMENT

fruit product, they might think twice about which bitem is best for them. All too often people choose snacks because they are making a quick decision. When people see that they are going to have to pay extra money, their thinking will likely change regarding which item to purchase.

Adding a tax to sugar products is another way to generate revenue for education and other public services.While some people might argue that this is simply unfair, it should be recognized that people are purchasing products they do not need.These sugary items are not necessities. They are wants. Taxing unnecessary items is a way to increase the state budget without punishing the population since people can decide whether or not to buy these items.For this reason, I am in support of a tax on sugary products.

Choosing to tax sugary products is a positive step towards creating a healthier population.Obesity and the number of people who are overweight is increasing at an alarming rate. When people are forced to pay more, they will hopefully choose healthier options. Some people may even learn that they like foods and drinks they have not previously tried after choosing new items instead of paying tax on sugary products.

Should a tax be passed on donuts, potato chips, candy bars, soda, and other sugary products? Yes! The decision to pass a tax on junk food will create more revenue for states, make people think twice about their snack choices, and aid people in consuming less empty calories.Let's take a stand to stop the sugar craze!

36. **One of the reasons the author feels sugary snacks should be taxed is to help create a healthier population. Which of the following statements is a detail included in the article to support this reason?**
(W.5.1 B)

   A. When people are forced to pay more, they will hopefully choose healthier options

   B. These sugary items are not necessities

   C. People may have skipped lunch or are looking for a quick snack to get them through the afternoon

   D. All too often people choose snacks because they are making a quick decision

END OF YEAR ASSESSMENT

37. **Which of the following statements about informational writing is FALSE?** (W.5.2)

   A. A conclusion paragraph is needed to restate one's opinion

   B. A conclusion sentence should wrap up each body paragraph

   C. A topic sentence is used to begin each body paragraph

   D. A thesis statement is an effective way to preview the body paragraphs' main points

38. **Which of the following words is an example of a domain-specific vocabulary that an author might use in a passage about outer space?** (W.5.3)

   A. orbit   **B.** galaxy   **C.** black hole   **D.** All of the above

> **Directions:** *Read the writing prompt and write your response in the space provided.*

=== **WRITING PROMPT** ===

39. Write a letter to your favorite teacher. (W.5.4)

_____

_____

_____

_____

_____

_____

_____

_____

END OF YEAR ASSESSMENT

_____

_____

_____

_____

_____

_____

_____

_____

_____

_____

_____

=== **MULTIPLE CHOICE** ===

40. Which of the following would NOTbe a reliable resource for conducting dinosaur fossil research? (W.5.7)

   A. An interview with an archaeologist

   B. A fairytale about dinosaurs

   C. A photo of real dinosaur fossils

   D. A historical fiction novel about dinosaur fossils

41. If you were preparing to write a research paper about the common cold, which of the following would be the best resource? (W.5.7)

   A. An article written by a doctor

   B. An article written by a sick patient

   C. A fiction novel about a boy who has a common cold

   D. An opinion piece about the common cold

END OF YEAR ASSESSMENT

> **Directions:** *Read the information from the webpage KidsHealth.org. Then answer the questions below.*

YOUR BONES

There are 206 bones in the human body. They protect you in many ways, and have many important functions, including cushioning your internal organs and helping you move. All of your bones connected together is called a skeleton. Have you ever seen a person dressed up as a skeleton for Halloween? That's what you look like on the inside!

WHAT ARE BONES MADE OF?

Old bones, or bones from the bodies of people who are no longer alive, are fragile, powdery, and dry. However, the bones of a living person are different - they are constantly developing and changing as you become older.

Your bones have a few layers to them. The outer layer is called the periosteum (par-ee-OSS-tee-um). The second layer, made of compact bone, is much harder, and has a smooth surface. This second layer is what you think of when you think of what bones look like. Inside the second layer are multiple layers of the inside bone, which is called cancellous bone (KAN-sell-us). This is a soft, spongy tissue that is filled with bone marrow, which is red.

HOW BONES GROW

When a baby is born, its body actually has more bones than an adult's - 300 bones, to be exact. That is because babies have a lot of growing and changing to do! Some of a baby's bones are made of cartilage (KAR_te_lij). You might have felt cartilage in your nose or ears. Cartilage is firm, but is still a lot softer than a regular bone. Overtime, some of a baby's cartilage is replaced by harder bones. Some of these bones fuse, or combine, to eventually become the 206 bones that an adult has.

END OF YEAR ASSESSMENT

YOUR SPINE

Your spine is one of the most important group of bones in your body. It protects your spinal cord, a group of nerves that connects your brain to your lower body. Your spine helps you move around, bend over to pick things up, and twist around. It is made up of vertebrae, smaller groups of bones (VER-tuh-bray).

=== **MULTIPLE CHOICE** ===

42. This webpage might be a good resource for researching which of the following topics? (W.5.8)

   A. The human skull   **B.** What bones are made of
   C. How bones grow   **D.** All the above

43. This webpage would NOT be helpful for researching which of the following topics? (W.5.8)

   A. Bone growth and development
   B. How bones break and mend
   C. The layers of the bone
   D. The location and function of the spine

44. What does the word *stationery* most likely mean? (L.5.4.A)

It contained his toothbrush, toothpaste, and a box of <u>stationery</u> his mother had given him. He'd promised to write to her once a week.

   A. Immovable   **B.** Notepaper   **C.** Gas station   **D.** Dictionary

END OF YEAR ASSESSMENT

> **Directions:** *Read the following and answer the questions below.*

FULL OF LIFE

FULL of life, now, compact, visible,
I, forty years old the Eighty-third Year of The States,
To one a century hence, or any number of centuries hence,
To you, yet unborn, these, seeking you.
When you read these, I, that was visible, am become invisible;
Now it is you, compact, visible, realizing my poems, seeking me;
Fancying how happy you were, if I could be with you,
and become your comrade;
Be it as if I were with you.
(Be not too certain but I am now with you.)

LIFE

LIFE, believe, is not a dream
So dark as sages say;
Oft a little morning rain
Foretells a pleasant day.
Sometimes there are clouds of gloom,
But these are transient all;
If the shower will make the roses bloom,
O why lament its fall?

Rapidly, merrily,
Life's sunny hours flit by,
Gratefully, cheerily,
Enjoy them as they fly!

...continued next page

     prepaze

END OF YEAR ASSESSMENT

What though Death at times steps
in And calls our Best away?
What though sorrow seems to win,
O'er hope, a heavy sway?
Yet hope again elastic springs,
Unconquered, though she fell; Still
buoyant are her golden wings, Still
strong to bear us well. Manfully,
fearlessly,
The day of trial bear,
For gloriously, victoriously,
Can courage quell despair!

══ MULTIPLE CHOICE ══

45. Which statement is true about the two passages? (RL. 5.9)

   A. The first passage is a poem and the second is a short story

   B. Both passages are poems

   C. The first passage is a short story and the second is a poem

   D. Both passages are short stories

ANSWER KEY

1. Reading: Literature

1.1. Key Ideas and Details................. 208

1.2. Craft and Structure.................... 209

1.3. Integration of Knowledge
      and Ideas 210

1.4. Chapter Review 211

2. Reading: Informational Text

2.1. Key Ideas and Details................. 213

2.2. Craft and Structure.................... 214

2.3. Integration of
      Knowledge and Ideas 215

2.4. Chapter Review 216

3. Reading: Foundational Skills

3.1. Phonics and Word Recognition 217

3.2. Chapter Review 218

4. Writing

4.1. Text Types and Purposes 220

4.2. Production and Distribution
      of Writing 221

4.3. Research to Build and
      Present Knowledge.................... 222

4.4. Chapter Review 223

5. Language

5.1. Conventions of
      Standard English...................... 225

5.2. Knowledge of Language 226

5.3. Vocabulary Acquisition
      and Use.................................. 228

5.4. Practice Test 229

End of Year Assessment 230

ANSWER KEY

1. READING: LITERATURE

1.1. Key Ideas and Details

1. Answer: B
Explanation: This line from the passage explains that David was startled because he heard a mouse scurrying overhead in the attic.

2. Answer: C
Explanation: Because David has to go to work in a few hours, he needs his sleep.

3. Answer: B
Explanation: The theme is the man (David) against nature (the mouse).

4. Answer: A
Explanation: The main event in the introduction is a mouse running around David's attic whereas the main event in the conclusion is David freeing the mouse outside.

5. Answer: D
Explanation: The passage does not go into detail about what the mouse looked like.

6. Answer: C
Explanation: The line best describes what the mousetrap looked like by describing the cheese on one end of the trap.

7. Answer: B
Explanation: David overcame the challenge of not being able to sleep due to the noise the mouse made by catching and releasing the mouse outside.

8. Answer: C
Explanation: The passage says that when David waits for the mouse to get stuck in the mousetrap, both are in the attic for 15 minutes.

9. Answer: C
Explanation: All answers are correct, but C best summarizes the passage.

10. Answer: A
Explanation: Because the mouse is scurrying back and forth in the attic, the reader can infer that the mouse is trying to find its way out of the attic.

11. Answer: B
Explanation: Even after her mom got the flu, Emma wanted to cook by herself so she could keep the family tradition going.

12. Answer: C
Explanation: By trying to cook breakfast by herself for the first time, Emma is showing that it is important to try your best and good things can happen.

13. Answer: C
Explanation: Because there were no eggs left, Emma would not be able to cook French toast and scrambled eggs.

14. Answer: A
Explanation: Emma and her mom cook the Sunday morning breakfast. Emma's dad and brothers only look forward to the tradition but do not help in the cooking.

15. Answer: B
Explanation: Because Emma is persistent in cooking alone, the reader can infer that family traditions are important to Emma and her family.

16. Answer: C
Explanation: The summary of the passage explains how Emma cooks breakfast by herself after her mom falls sick to keep the tradition alive.

17. Answer: B
Explanation: The challenge in the passage is that Emma had to cook by herself.

18. Answer: B
Explanation: In paragraph 2 Emma ponders the breakfast menu.

ANSWER KEY

19. Answer: A

Explanation: Emma first learns she has to cook by herself and then accomplishes that task by making Sunday breakfast for her entire family.

20. Answer: A

Explanation: The passage does not explain why Emma's dad and brothers do not offer to help her in place of her mom's absence.

1.2. Craft and Structure

1. Answer: A

Explanation: The cook's actions of boiling the child show her anger and ill-will.

2. Answer: B

Explanation: Bring him up means to raise a child.

3. Answer: C

Explanation: The forester came across as very nice to both his child and the one he kidnapped.

4. Answer: A

Explanation: This would be a problem in the story when the old cook is planning on harming the child.

5. Answer: B

Explanation: Fetch has many different meanings, but in this case, it means to bring back in order for the old cook to start her plan.

6. Answer: D

Explanation: Her actions of not keeping the secret show she cares for Fundevogel.

7. Answer: Show the old cook's idea since her plan did not work.

Explanation: Including a monologue is better than just describing it in this story so that it shows it comes straight from the character.

8. Answer: Her violent plan towards Fundevogel when she tries to boil him in a kettle.

Explanation: Old Sanna is a character that the narrator does not like and is afraid of.

9. Answer: D

Explanation: The multiple changes are included in order to show that the children could trick the servants multiple times.

10. Answer: A

Explanation: Old Sanna is shown to be cruel not only to the children but also to the servants.

11. Answer: B

Explanation: Old Sanna, the old cook, wants the servants to catch them and bring them back.

12. Answer: A

Explanation: The Old Cook is old, so she would have trouble getting up.

13. Answer: C

Explanation: This poem is sarcastic and shows the bad foods the boy ate even though he states that he gave that food to his stomach as a gift.

14. Answer: A

Explanation: The last stanza shows that the boy gets sick enough to have to take terrible-tasting medicine.

15. Answer: The narrator's viewpoint of the stomach is that it is acting in its normal capacity and behavior.It is not doing anything different than it normally does. It is the reaction of the boy that makes the poem.

Explanation: This poem has actually two characters:the boy and the stomach.

ANSWER KEY

16. Answer: It means that he fed himself things that he thought his stomach would like because they tasted so good even though they were bad for him.

Explanation: Many of the items that were mentioned are desserts or sweets.

17. Answer: A

Explanation: The author wants to show the interactions between the servant and the neighbor.

18. Answer: C

Explanation: The neighbor is rude by the way he comes across to the servant who answers the door.

19. Answer: D

Explanation: The neighbor's way of coming to the door to hand over a gift to the servant is becoming increasingly worse each time.

20. Answer: B

Explanation: Partridges are birds that are sometimes used for food.

1.3. Integration of Knowledge and Ideas

1. Answer: D

Explanation: The picture illustrates Peter squeezing under the gate.

2. Answer: A

Explanation: The picture illustrates Peter stuck in the gooseberry net.

3. Answer: C

Explanation: The rabbit in the picture is not wearing the little coat his mother gave him and is carrying an Easter egg and flowers, neither of which are mentioned in the passage.

4. Answer: C

Explanation: The characters in the picture are Strong Arm and the funny little boy.

5. Answer: C

Explanation: The picture illustrates the giant carrying their father away.

6. Answer: C

Explanation: Both A and B can be found in the passages.Both heroines demonstrate that inner beauty is as valuable as outer beauty.Both stepmothers demonstrate that jealousy can cause people to do terrible things.

7. Answer: C

Explanation: Both themes of the value of inner beauty and the problems of jealousy are apparent.

8. Answer: B

Explanation: Both passages are written in third person point of view.

9. Answer: C

Explanation: Both Cinderella and Snow White are patient and compassionate toward their stepmothers even when the stepmothers are mean to them.

10. Answer: A

Explanation: The Fairy Godmother using her magic wand to turn a pumpkin into a carriage in Cinderella and the talking mirror in Snow White each show evidence of fantasy in the passages.

11. Answer: A

Explanation: Hansel threw stones out of his pocket on the road.

12. Answer: C

Explanation: The birds ate the breadcrumbs.

13. Answer: D

Explanation: The picture with the giant.

prep☉ze

www.prepaze.com

ANSWER KEY

14. Answer: A

Explanation: The picture illustrates the old woman coming out of her house.

15. Answer: C

Explanation: The presentation would not require this information, since the assignment was to summarize the plot. The woodcutter's job is not the main detail and is not mentioned.

16. Answer: D

Explanation: The first passage is written in third person point of view and the second is written in first person.

17. Answer: A

Explanation: The Little Red Hen and the second speaker are both willing to work.

18. Answer: C

Explanation: The first passage is a short story and the second is a poem.

19. Answer: A

Explanation: Both authors use personification in their writing. The main characters of both passages are animals who speak.

20. Answer: A

Explanation: The first passage contains dialogue between several characters while the second is a monologue where the speaker is speaking to her owner.

1.4. Chapter Review

1. Answer: A

Explanation: The Dean learns the lesson that he has acted badly so the narrator is negative towards him.

2. Answer: A

Explanation: The Dean also realized that he should have given him a monetary tip which he had not done in the past.

3. Answer: B

Explanation: Since this story is true, the last few lines want to inform the reader about whose true story this is.

4. Answer: A

Explanation: One time of rudeness could be a one-time deal, so the story includes multiple times to prove that this was an act of rudeness.

5. Answer: B

Explanation: The first part shows who the King is and a little bit about him so the reader can understand the story.

6. Answer: A

Explanation: The King is brave because he is used to so many bombs going off.

7. Answer: D

Explanation: This may be exaggerated, but it would show how serious the King was about his job and how he was used to war.

8. Answer: C

Explanation: The King would force the officer to sit down and continue despite the danger.

9. Answer: D

Explanation: Spry refers to something that is lively and active.

10. Answer: A

Explanation: The mountain name calls the squirrel to show that it is little and the mountain is big.

11. Answer: C

Explanation: The squirrel mentions that it is able to crack a nut and the mountain would not be able to do that.

12. Answer: D

Explanation: The squirrel proves its worth even though it is so small.

13. Answer: C

Explanation: The summary of the passage is that Austin competed in the

Copyrighted Material **prepaze**

ANSWER KEY

championships to make his family proud and when he fell, his dad told him he was still a winner.

14. Answer: D
Explanation: The passage says Austin was 4 inches shorter than his dad but did not say how tall he was.

15. Answer: C
Explanation: Austin's dad was a superstar athlete while Austin was not.

16. Answer: D
Explanation: Austin overcame his nervousness and was able to make his dad proud.

17. Answer: D
Explanation: Austin feels nervous in paragraph 4 and upset in paragraph 5.

18. Answer: C
Explanation: After he fell, Austin's dad knew his son was upset and needed to be encouraged.

19. Answer: C
Explanation: The main theme of the passage is to get back up after you fall just like Austin did.

20. Answer: B
Explanation: How tall he is doesn't matter specifically. Because height was a major factor in his sport, Austin struggled in his events.

21. Answer: C
Explanation: Austin goes from being nervous at the start of the race to being comforted at the end.

22. Answer: B
Explanation: Austin's dad tells him he is a winner.

23. Answer: B
Explanation: The championship meet takes place during the morning and Austin

fell during his first event so it couldn't be evening yet.

24. Answer: A
Explanation: Because training for his events was his main focus, Austin is showing to the reader that he is a determined athlete.

25. Answer: D
Explanation: The first passage is a narration about a legend; the second is a myth.

26. Answer: B
Explanation: The war in the first passage was the war between the elements (ice and fire) while the war in the second passage was between gods and Titans.

27. Answer: B
Explanation: The first passage explains the origination of giants, while the second passage describes a war in which the giants fought alongside the Titans.

28. Answer: C
Explanation: The picture that illustrates Timmy landing on the dinner table.

29. Answer: A
Explanation: The picture illustrates the cook opening the hamper.

30. Answer: D
Explanation: Timmy broke three glasses landing on the dinner party.

ANSWER KEY

2. READING: INFORMATIONAL TEXT

2.1. Key Ideas and Details

1. Answer: B
Explanation: Because they were nomadic, Apaches traveled and moved quite often.

2. Answer: C
Explanation: Although all of the choices are true, the best one that describes the main idea is answer c that refers to the types of housing.

3. Answer: B
Explanation: The fact that winters were harsh is not directly addressed and is not a key detail in the text.

4. Answer: A
Explanation: Both teepees and wickiups were made from wooden frames.

5. Answer: D
Explanation: The text describes what wickiups and hogans were covered with but not teepees.

6. Answer: A
Explanation: Because they were nomadic and moved around, their style of living did not create cities.

7. Answer: B
Explanation: Overall, the text describes the rich culture of the Apaches.

8. Answer: C
Explanation: Both the Apaches of today and those 600 years ago are working/have worked to maintain their ancient culture.

9. Answer: D
Explanation: The mud and clay helped provide shelter in the cold and kept them warm. Therefore, both A & B are correct.

10. Answer: D
Explanation: Answers B & C are the most correct choices. The first option is too vague.

11. Answer: A
Explanation: The text mentions the temperature is 80 degrees in a rainforest so the reader can infer that rainforests have warm climates.

12. Answer: B
Explanation: A main idea of the text is that plants have developed adaptations to stay alive in rainforests.

13. Answer: A
Explanation: This line refers to how plants have needed to adapt to the conditions in the rainforest.

14. Answer: B
Explanation: Epiphytes get their nutrients from the air while parasitic plants get them from other plants that they live on.

15. Answer: B
Explanation: Because plants grow quickly, they must adapt to get enough nutrients to survive.

16. Answer: D
Explanation: Each answer is correct.

17. Answer: A
Explanation: A second main idea in the text is the depletion of nutrients in the soil.

18. Answer: D
Explanation: Both paragraphs 2 & 3 describe plant adaptations for epiphytes and parasitic plants.

19. Answer: D
Explanation: Mosses and orchids are both epiphytes that get their nutrients from the air.

20. Answer: C
Explanation: The text does not explain the second adaptation.

prepaze

2. READING: INFORMATIONAL TEXT

ANSWER KEY

2.2. Craft and Structure

1. Answer: B
Explanation: The word *peninsula* most likely means *a piece of land* in the context of this text.

2. Answer: D
Explanation: The word *population* most likely means *the number of residents* in the context of this text.

3. Answer: A
Explanation: The phrase *the continent reaches* most likely means that the continent is closely located next to Chile and Argentina.

4. Answer: B
Explanation: The phrase *under consideration* most likely means *being thought about* in the context of this text.

5. Answer: C
Explanation: The text structure in passage 1 is best described as compare and contrast.

6. Answer: C
Explanation: The text structure in passage 2 is best described as descriptive.

7. Answer: A
Explanation: These passages share the same topic. Both passages are mainly about dogs.

8. Answer: B
Explanation: Passage 1 is an informational text. Passage 2 is a persuasive text.

9. Answer: A
Explanation: Passage 1 is a chronological text, while passage 2 is a descriptive text.

10. Answer: B
Explanation: Passage 1 is written in the first person, while passage 2 is written in the third person.

11. Answer: B
Explanation: Both passages describe the Grand Canyon's appearance.

12. Answer: A
Explanation: The word *atmosphere* most likely means *surroundings* in the context of this text.

13. Answer: C
Explanation: The word *funds* most likely means *money* in the context of this text.

14. Answer: B
Explanation: The word *quality* most likely means *value* in the context of this text.

15. Answer: A
Explanation: The word *advertised* most likely means *marketed* in the context of this text.

16. Answer: D
Explanation: The word *involved* most likely means *participating* in the context of this text.

17. Answer: C
Explanation: The text structure found in paragraph 1 is best described as descriptive.

18. Answer: A
Explanation: The text structure found in paragraph 1 is best described as cause and effect.

19. Answer: B
Explanation: Both paragraphs share the same topic.

20. Answer: B
Explanation: Paragraph 1 explains fluoride use history and Paragraph 2 how it works.

ANSWER KEY

2.3. Integration of Knowledge and Ideas

1. Answer: A
Explanation: The information explains the difference between black bears and brown bears.

2. Answer: D
Explanation: A website about bear appearances and characteristics would best accompany this information.

3. Answer: C
Explanation: The picture shows physical details about bears.

4. Answer: A
Explanation: The passage does not explain what grizzly bears eat.

5. Answer: C
Explanation: Both texts state facts about Honduras.

6. Answer: A
Explanation: You could learn about the 4 regions of Honduras from reading these texts.

7. Answer: B
Explanation: Passage 2 offers the most information about popular hobbies in Honduras.

8. Answer: A
Explanation: Passage 1 offers the most information about countries surrounding Honduras.

9. Answer: Pollution
Explanation: According to the text, there are three categories of pollution sources.

10. Answer: Area
Explanation: According to the chart, 32% of pollution comes from buildings, or area sources.

11. Answer: Answers may vary.
Explanation: Students should be able to explain how multiple resources can be used to develop a topic. For example, the chart shows a visual representation of the information from the text.

12. Answer: B
Explanation: The texts contain information about the Triceratops's diet.

13. Answer: D
Explanation: The texts do not mention the Triceratops's skin and scales.

14. Answer: A
Explanation: An encyclopedia page about Triceratops would best accompany this information.

15. Answer: D
Explanation: All of these digital sources could accompany this information.

16. Answer: B
Explanation: This statement is false. It is best to refer to multiple resources per topic.

17. Answer: A
Explanation: This statement is true. Both a magazine article and a website can be used to find information about flowers.

18. Answer: A
Explanation: This statement is true. An internet keyword search can be a quick way to find answers.

19. Answer: B
Explanation: This statement is false. A thesaurus would not be the best resource for locating a map of Australia. A thesaurus is a resource for finding word meanings, synonyms and antonyms.

20. Answer: B
Explanation: This statement is false. Two texts written by different authors can offer the same information.

2. READING: INFORMATIONAL TEXT

ANSWER KEY

2.4. Chapter Review

1. Answer: D
Explanation: Both passages share all of these topics.

2. Answer: C
Explanation: Passage 1 presents a chronological timeline of segregation, while passage 2 tells a story about characters living in that era.

3. Answer: A
Explanation: Both passages describe the same events, but from different points-of-view.

4. Answer: B
Explanation: The word *implemented* most likely means *enforced* in the context of this text.

5. Answer: A
Explanation: This statement is true. Academic word meanings can found through text evidence.

6. Answer: A
Explanation: This statement is true. Both the compare/contrast and the problem/solution text structures explore two or more parts of a subject.

7. Answer: B
Explanation: This statement is false. Multiple accounts of the same event can be presented from different points-of-view.

8. Answer: B
Explanation: This statement is false. A narrative text will most likely differ in structure, but can have the same point-of-view as an informational text.

9. Answer: C
Explanation: A dictionary and a thesaurus would be the best resources for finding word meanings.

10. Answer: A
Explanation: A website about planets and a picture of Jupiter would be the best resources for finding this information.

11. Answer: B
Explanation: An opinion piece would not be a good resource for finding facts about tornados.

12. Answer: C
Explanation: These article would offer the best information about preventing sunburn.

13. Answer: D
Explanation: A website about recipes would not help you find information about feeding a pet turtle.

14. Answer: A
Explanation: A Chinese dictionary and a translation website would be the best resources for learning to speak Chinese.

15. Answer: C
Explanation: The word *alerted* most likely means *made aware of* in the context of this text.

16. Answer: A
Explanation: The word *expedition* most likely means *mission* in the context of this text.

17. Answer: C
Explanation: The word *decline* most likely means *reduction* in the context of this text.

18. Answer: D
Explanation: The word *incredible* most likely means *unbelievable* in the context of this text.

19. Answer: C
Explanation: This choice gives the most complete answer: Rosa's actions led to the Montgomery Bus Boycott, which led to the Supreme Court decision.

prepaze

www.prepaze.com

20. Answer: D
Explanation: The text does not explain what the Jim Crow laws were.

21. Answer: B
Explanation: Parks inspired King and other Civil Rights leaders.

22. Answer: A
Explanation: One main idea is that Rosa Parks' arrest led to the bus boycott.

23. Answer: B
Explanation: Paragraph 2 & 3 best describes the bus boycott.

24. Answer: B
Explanation: The reader can infer that Rosa Parks was brave after standing up for herself and getting arrested.

25. Answer: A
Explanation: A second main idea of the text was that the bus boycott led to the Supreme Court ruling.

26. Answer: D
Explanation: This line best describes the support for Parks given that black commuters walked more than 20 miles.

27. Answer: A
Explanation: This choice provides the most complete answer: Parks' arrest led to the start of the bus boycott which led to the Supreme Court ruling which ended bus segregation.

28. Answer: B
Explanation: The second choice is a key detail because it mentions an important event- Rosa refusing to give up her seat.

29. Answer: A
Explanation: The reader can infer the importance of the bus boycott on U.S. history.

30. Answer: A
Explanation: Both Parks and King were significant figures in the civil rights movement in America.

3. READING: FOUNDATIONAL SKILLS

3.1. Phonics and Word Recognition

1. Answer: C
Explanation: The word "revise" means to look over something again to correct or improve it.

2. Answer: C
Explanation: The word "automatic" means starting by itself; done without thought; routine.

3. Answer: C
Explanation: The word "perspective" means the way someone looks at things.

4. Answer: D
Explanation: The word "ordinary" means normal; usual; regular; dull.

5. Answer: C
Explanation: The root "mille" means one thousand.

6. Answer: B
Explanation: The word "unique" means one-of-a-kind; single; rare; special.

7. Answer: D
Explanation: The word "restrictions" means to set limits.

8. Answer: A
Explanation: The word "degrade" means to reduce or lower.

9. Answer: B
Explanation: The word "distinct" means to be clearly different.

10. Answer: D
Explanation: The word "protect" means to keep safe; defend.

3. READING: FOUNDATIONAL SKILLS

prepaze

ANSWER KEY

11. Answer: A

Explanation: The word "forbidden" does mean not permitted; banned.

12. Answer: A

Explanation: The word "ejected" does mean to have pushed something out with force.

13. Answer: B

Explanation: The word "elevation" does not mean the circumference of a mountain. It refers to the height of a mountain.

14. Answer: B

Explanation: The word "seize" does not mean to let go of something slowly. It means to take hold of something; grab; capture.

15. Answer: A

Explanation: The word "acre" does mean a unit of area.

16. Answer: The student will define the word sensitive.

Explanation: "Sensitive" means easily upset by others' remarks or behaviors.

17. Answer: The student will define the word obstacle.

Explanation: "Obstacle" means something in way; hurdle; barrier; blockage.

18. Answer: The student will define the word antique.

Explanation: "Antique" means old; vintage; classic.

19. Answer: The student will define the word unexpected.

Explanation: "Unexpected" means surprising.

20. Answer: The student will define the word apology.

Explanation: "Apology" means statement expressing remorse; say sorry.

3.2. Chapter Review

1. Answer: A

Explanation: The word *photosynthesis* means "the process of using sunlight to make food."

2. Answer: C

Explanation: The word *emit* means "to send forth or release." The phrase "light-emitting" refers to something that releases light.

3. Answer: B

Explanation: The letters *t* and *u* make the irregular /ch/ sound in the word *future*.

4. Answer: D

Explanation: The *ar* + silent *e* combination makes the "air" sound in the word *warehouse*.

5. Answer: A

Explanation: The letters *al* make the /ul/ sound in the words *vertical* and *principal*.

6. Answer: A

Explanation: The word *climate* has an open syllable pattern. In the open syllable pattern the syllable ends in a vowel (cli + mate).

7. Answer: C

Explanation: The word *harvest* has an r-controlled syllable pattern. In the r-controlled syllable pattern, a vowel is followed by *r* which affects the sound of the vowel. The vowel and the *r* will appear in the same syllable (har + vest).

8. Answer: D

Explanation: The word *fertilizer* has 4 syllables. The first syllable is r-controlled and should be divided after the *r*. The following syllables are divided by the V/CV and VC/V patterns. The word should be divided as fer + ti + liz + er.

9. Answer: assistance

Explanation: The suffix -ance should be added to the word *assist* to show "the act of" rather than "a person who." She needs some assistance with her science project.

10. Answer: tricycle

Explanation: The Latin prefix uni- means "one." It should be replaced with the prefix tri- which means "three." I purchased a new tricycle with three wheels.

11. Answer: leadership

Explanation: The suffix -ship is the best way to show "a condition of" with the word *leader*. This suffix indicates that the person has a certain skill related to the condition. Walter was rewarded for his leadership in the community.

12. Answer: disrupted or interrupted

Explanation: The word *erupt* means "to burst or force out." The prefix dis- (or inter-) should be added to the root *rupt* to show that something caused a negative change or came in between an action. The movie was disrupted (interrupted) by a loud noise from the audience.

13. Answer: photograph

Explanation: The root *graph* means "to write or record." An autograph is someone's own handwriting. A photograph is picture taken by a camera. We took many photographs of the beach while on vacation.

14. Answer: B

Explanation: The rhyme scheme of the first four lines is AABB. In this rhyme scheme, each subsequent pair of lines (such as 1 and 2) rhyme.

15. Answer: A

Explanation: This poem is best read aloud with a gloomy or melancholy expression. Students should recognize how expression affects the way a poem is read aloud.

16. Answer: C

Explanation: The word *former* has double consonants in the middle of the word. It should be divided by the VC/CV pattern

(for + mer).

17. Answer: C

Explanation: The word *cake* has a vowel + consonant + silent *e* combination. It should be divided by the VCe pattern. In this syllable pattern, the silent *e* will appear in the same syllable with the vowel and consonant that it affects (cake).

18. Answer: B

Explanation: This statement is false. A multisyllabic word is pronounced in multiple units of sound.

19. Answer: B

Explanation: This statement is false. Prose is often written in a free verse style and does not have a strict rhyme scheme.

20. Answer: A

Explanation: This statement is true. The word hammock has a closed syllable pattern. In this pattern, the syllables end in a consonant.

21. Answer: A

Explanation: This statement is true. The Greek root dict means "to say."

22. Answer: peeks

Explanation: The word *peeks* is used incorrectly in this sentence. The word *peaks* should be used in this context.

23. Answer: presence

Explanation: The word *presence* is used incorrectly in this sentence. The word *presents* should be used in this context.

24. Answer: meddle

Explanation: The word *meddle* is used incorrectly in this sentence. The word *medal* should be used in this context.

25. Answer: weather

Explanation: The word *weather* is used incorrectly in this sentence. The word *whether* should be used in this context.

3. READING: FOUNDATIONAL SKILLS

prepaze

ANSWER KEY

26. Answer: A
Explanation: When alternate lines rhyme in a poem (1 and 3, 2 and 4) this is called an ABAB rhyme scheme.

27. Answer: D
Explanation: The Latin prefix inter- means "between."

28. Answer: B
Explanation: The Greek suffix -logy means "the study of."

29. Answer: C
Explanation: The word fable has a C + le syllable pattern. In this pattern, the letters *le* appear in the same syllable with the consonant that it affects (fa + ble).

30. Answer: B
Explanation: The word *migrate* should be divided in the V/CV syllable pattern. The word is divided after the long vowel sound in the first syllable (mi + grate).

4. WRITING

4.1. Text Types and Purposes

1. Answer: B
Explanation: The author states the online learning is beneficial for learners who truly want to be prepared for future careers.

2. Answer: A
Explanation: This detail would not support the author's claim that online learning is beneficial.

3. Answer: B
Explanation: The consequence of online learning is the lack of hands-on experience.

4. Answer: A
Explanation: "In brief" is a transition that is used to connect one idea to another.

5. Answer: D
Explanation: This option clearly states the author's opinion.

6. Answer: D
Explanation: While the author provides some reasons to support their claim, these reasons are unelaborated and are not supported with research.Using research and discussing why someone might disagree with him or her is an essential part of an argument.

7. Answer: B
Explanation: A counterclaim would present the opposing side's viewpoint and a rebuttal would weaken the counterclaim. These components are not presented in the passage.

8. Answer: A
Explanation: This detail clearly shows how online learning programs increase flexibility.

9. Answer: C
Explanation: Since the focus is on its label as a "barrier peninsula", it would be beneficial to provide a diagram to show what this landform actually is.

10. Answer: A
Explanation: Headings are used to introduce the main ideas which are part of the body paragraphs.

11. Answer: B
Explanation: A quotation should be from a reputable source.Often times this should be an expert in the field.

12. Answer: D
Explanation: Informational writing should be presented to teach about a topic.It should be free from opinions.

13. Answer: A
Explanation: The transition 'in contrast' shows how these two people were different.

ANSWER KEY

14. Answer: B

Explanation: The transition 'additionally' shows that the two ideas are linked and build on each other.

15. Answer: B

Explanation: The reader can picture someone who is friendly and usually smiling.

16. Answer: A

Explanation: This passage would be about informing about the problem or even arguing that something needs to be done to reach a resolution.

17. Answer: D

Explanation: This option presents a description of the character. The other options are informative and are directly related to teaching about the topic, rather than storytelling.

18. Answer: C

Explanation: But is a word to introduce a contrasting idea.

19. Answer: D

Explanation: The mortals were described as "leading a wretched life and were unconscious of the spiritual or intellectual gifts conferred upon them by their creator. and that they were like beasts.

20. Answer: C

Explanation: The events happened in the following order, 1,3,4,2

4.2. Production and Distribution of Writing

1. Answer: D

Explanation: The author was most likely asked to write a letter to the local waste management agency.

2. Answer: B

Explanation: The author was most likely asked to write a thank-you note to his or her birthday party guests.

3. Answer: C

Explanation: The author was most likely asked to write about his or her personal views on professional sports.

4. Answer: A

Explanation: The author was most likely asked to write a letter to the school cafeteria.

5. Answer: C

Explanation: The Spelling and Grammar Checker is found on the Review tab in Microsoft Word.

6. Answer: D

Explanation: All of these tasks can be accomplished with the Spelling and Grammar Checker.

7. Answer: A

Explanation: The text states that the feature makes suggestions to help you correct spelling and grammar errors.

8. Answer: C

Explanation: This feature can change more than one error at a time. The text states that there is a "Change All" feature.

9. Answer: A

Explanation: This statement is true. The writing style may differ based on task, purpose, and audience.

10. Answer: B

Explanation: This statement is false. It is best to plan the organization of your paper before you start writing.

11. Answer: A

Explanation: This statement is true. Correcting misspelled words is an example of editing.

4. WRITING

ANSWER KEY

12. Answer: A

Explanation: This statement is true. Kindle is an example of an E-book reader.

13. Answer: B

Explanation: This statement is false. Dictionary.com is an example of a website. Yourname123@website.com is an example of an email address.

14. Answer: C

Explanation: The text is most likely an opinion piece written by a student.

15. Answer: B

Explanation: This sentence is missing a comma after the linking phrase "for instance."

16. Answer: D

Explanation: This sentence is not relevant to the topic of the text.

17. Answer: C

Explanation: This is most likely a document created with Microsoft Word.

18. Answer: Answers will vary.

Explanation: Students should demonstrate the ability to use technology for writing tasks. Ex: First type the word "France" into the search bar.

19. Answer: Answers will vary.

Explanation: Students should demonstrate the ability to use technology for writing tasks. Ex: Click on the "File" tab and then click "Save As."

20. Answer: Answers will vary.

Explanation: Students should demonstrate an understanding of how to revise their writing. Some examples include adding/removing words and sentences.

4.3. Research to Build and Present Knowledge

1. Answer: B

Explanation: This is a historical fiction novel and can be used when researching the time era.

2. Answer: D

Explanation: This would be a good resource for researching all of these topics.

3. Answer: C

Explanation: A history book about Harlem would be the best resource for researching this topic.

4. Answer: C

Explanation: Aunt Odessa would not appear in your bibliography. A bibliography includes information about the resource (title, author, etc.), not characters in the story.

5. Answer: B

Explanation: This statement is false. It is best to write down key information when taking notes.

6. Answer: B

Explanation: This statement is false. Literary texts, such as historical fiction novels, can be used for conducting research.

7. Answer: A

Explanation: This statement is true. It is best to refer to multiple resources when conducting research.

8. Answer: A

Explanation: This statement is true. A text can be summarized by restating the key points in your notes.

9. Answer: A

Explanation: This statement is true. You could refer to an article by the American

ANSWER KEY

Dental Association when writing an essay about oral health.

10. Answer: A
Explanation: Both the diagram and the article demonstrate the order of the life cycle.

11. Answer: C
Explanation: The sentence "After this period of 21 days of incubation, the egg breaks and the wet chick cracks the shell and enters this world" offers the best information about hatching.

12. Answer: B
Explanation: The following sentence best summarizes the text: The chicken begins life as an egg and, after 6 months of development, becomes an adult.

13. Answer: D
Explanation: A video showing the life cycle of a real chicken would also be helpful when researching this topic.

14. Answer: Answers will vary.
Explanation: Students should be able to gather key information from a text and use it to write notes.

15. Answer: Answers will vary.
Explanation: Students should be able to explain how and why they selected specific information from the text.

16. Answer: Answers will vary.
Explanation: Students should be able to use information from the text, and personal experiences, as a source of research. They should also be able to avoid plagiarism and cite resources in their writing.

17. Answer: B
Explanation: The article, "The Dangers of Skateboarding" would be the best resource to support your argument.

18. Answer: D
Explanation: All of these resources .would be helpful for writing a historical fiction

story. Historical fiction is based on real events.

19. Answer: C
Explanation: A TV documentary about Egyptians hieroglyphs and symbols would be the best resource for researching the topic.

20. Answer: A
Explanation: The Top 3 Best Lasagna Recipes would be the best resource for researching the topic.

4.4. Chapter Review

1. Answer: D
Explanation: The transition 'for example' shows that the second detail is building on the first one.The sentence about Kentucky is a specific example that relates to the first sentence.

2. Answer: D
Explanation: Both of these words can be used to complete the sentence. Meanwhile shows a difference or contrasting statement and would not correctly complete the sentence.

3. Answer: C
Explanation: The transition 'specifically' would accurately complete this sentence. For example, would not be used since the information is being built on the previous sentence.It is not really an example.

4. Answer: D
Explanation: The word 'nocturnal' would not relate to the topic.

5. Answer: B
Explanation: The sentence, "Country music is very festive and entertaining" would most likely appear in an opinion piece. This sentence expresses an opinion.

4. WRITING

ANSWER KEY

6. Answer: A

Explanation: The sentence, "The Washington Bluebirds are expected to win the championship" would most likely appear in a newspaper article. This sentence uses formal language which is appropriate for this type of writing.

7. Answer: C

Explanation: The sentence, "Mr. Franklin, please consider making changes to the city's pet ordinance" would most likely appear in a letter to a politician. This sentence directly addresses the person reading the letter.

8. Answer: D

Explanation: The sentence, "Once the water begins to boil rapidly, place the pasta into the pot" would most likely appear in a recipe. This sentence is explanatory and list steps.

9. Answer: B

Explanation: The author believes sugary foods should be taxed because they are not a necessity.

10. Answer: D

Explanation: The main point of the second paragraph is that if sugary snacks were taxed, buyers might consider healthier snacks that are not taxed.

11. Answer: A

Explanation: The author must support his or her claim (assertion) with accurate, relevant research.Without appropriate support, the opinion cannot be proven.

12. Answer: D

Explanation: All of these statements are false.Opinion writing is also a form of persuasive writing.It requires developing an assertion with clear, accurate research.

13. Answer: C

Explanation: Sentence 6 contains a spelling error. The word *fatigued* is misspelled.

14. Answer: B

Explanation: Sentence 3 contains a punctuation error. This sentence needs a comma to separate the clauses.

15. Answer: D

Explanation: Sentence 8 contains a grammatical error. The verb phrase *have been* should be replaced with *will be.* The word *tomorrow* indicates that something will happen in the future. The verb phrase should also indicate future actions.

16. Answer: A

Explanation: Sentence 4 contains a capitalization error. The name Garcia is a proper noun and should be capitalized.

17. Answer: A

Explanation: Passage 1 contains more information about Mandela's birth name.

18. Answer: B

Explanation: Passage 2 contains more information about Mandela's parents.

19. Answer: C

Explanation: The sentence "He was born in the Xhosa-speaking village of Mvezo, South Africa, and was the Thembu tribe's chief's son." is the best example of paraphrasing.

20. Answer: D

Explanation: When he was a child, he was called "Rolihlahla." This name can mean two things: "pulling the branch of a tree" or "troublemaker." is not an example of paraphrasing. This is the exact statement from the text.

21. Answer: B

Explanation: "Who will make the bread?" is an example of dialogue.

22. Answer: C

Explanation: Finally is a sequence word that signals the final event in a series.

ANSWER KEY

23. Answer: C
Explanation: The passage about the Little Red Hen ended with the little Red Hen eating her bread alone. She did not share with the other animals because they did not help make it.

24. Answer: D
Explanation: Basically presenting the conclusion is the place for the resolution. All of the loose ends in the story should be resolved.

25. Answer: Desktop Shortcut
Explanation: To open a document in Microsoft Word, you can browse the Start Menu or create a desktop shortcut.

26. Answer: Startup
Explanation: The blank document template is located on the Startup screen.

27. Answer: Title
Explanation: After you type in your title, you should save your document.

28. Answer: Autosave
Explanation: The Auto Save function periodically saves your work in case of a computer crash.

29. Answer: C
Explanation: An article about a recent dinosaur fossil discovery would be the best resource for researching this topic.

30. Answer: D
Explanation: All of these resources would be helpful for researching this topic.

5. LANGUAGE

5.1. Conventions of Standard English

1. Answer: C
Explanation: The word *behind* is a preposition used to indicate the location of the bushes.

2. Answer: B
Explanation: John has been singing in the choir since he was 9 years old. The verb phrase *has been singing* is in the past perfect progressive tense, and agrees with the ongoing actions that occurred in the past.

3. Answer: C
Explanation: I have known Mr. Johnson for a very long time. The verb phrase *have known* is in the present perfect tense and agree with present actions that began in the past.

4. Answer: A
Explanation: The sentence, "He will be visiting us for the past two weeks" has an inappropriate shift in verb tense. The verb phrase *will be visiting* is in the future tense and does not agree with past actions as indicated in the phrase "past two weeks."

5. Answer: B
Explanation: You can either ride the train or take a taxicab.

6. Answer: The restaurant has locations in Phoenix, Arizona; Dallas, Texas; and Los Angeles, California.
Explanation: Students should be able to accurately use punctuation to separate list items in a sentence. This sentence requires commas and semicolons.

5. LANGUAGE

ANSWER KEY

7. Answer: Afterwards, he went home to take a nap.

Explanation: Students should be able to accurately separate introductory words/ phrases from the rest of the sentence.

8. Answer: No, I would not like ketchup on my hamburger.

Explanation: Students should be able to accurately set off words/phrases from the rest of the sentence. The words *yes* and *no* should be set off with a comma.

9. Answer: A

Explanation: Article titles should appear in quotation marks.

10. Answer: C

Explanation: *Avalanche* is the correct spelling of the underlined word.

11. Answer: B

Explanation: *Hooray* is an interjection used to show excitement.

12. Answer: D

Explanation: I cooked dinner and washed the dishes last night. The verb *cooked* is in the simple past tense and agrees with the past actions that occurred yesterday.

13. Answer: B

Explanation: Valerie had been living in that home for many years before she moved. The verb phrase *had been living* is in the past perfect progressive tense and agrees with past actions that occurred before another action.

14. Answer: C

Explanation: The sentence, "Bianca has joined the basketball team next year" has an inappropriate verb shift. The verb phrase *has joined* is in the past tense and does not agree with future actions as indicated in the phrase "next year."

15. Answer: C

Explanation: Neither Suzy nor Mario have seen the lost kitten.

16. Answer: The casserole recipe requires cheese, broccoli, chicken and rice.

Explanation: Students should be able to accurately use punctuation to separate list items in a sentence. This sentence requires commas.

17. Answer: As a matter of fact, I think that Mr. Washington is quite a good teacher.

Explanation: Students should be able to accurately separate introductory words/ phrases from the rest of the sentence.

18. Answer: You would like to order a vanilla milkshake, correct?

Explanation: Students should be able to accurately set off words/phrases from the rest of the sentence. The word *correct* is a tag question and should be set off with a comma.

19. Answer: B

Explanation: Movie titles should be italicized.

20. Answer: B

Explanation: *Compensated* is the correct spelling of the underlined word.

5.2. Knowledge of Language

1. Answer: Michael has green eyes and brown hair.

Explanation: Students should be able to accurately combine two or more sentences.

2. Answer: I ate a sandwich, an apple, and carrots for lunch today.

Explanation: Students should be able to accurately combine two or more sentences.

3. Answer: Whales, bears, and tigers are mammals.

Explanation: Students should be able to accurately combine two or more sentences.

ANSWER KEY

4. Answer: Cindy's sister, Maggie, is her identical twin.

Explanation: Students should be able to accurately reduce sentences by removing unnecessary words/phrases. The phrase "because identical means the same" is not necessary in this sentence.

5. Answer: Answers will vary.

Explanation: Students should be able to accurately reduce sentences by removing unnecessary words/phrases. Since all of these words have the same meaning, one or more can be removed in order to reduce the sentence. Ex.: The girl was crying because she was extremely sad and blue.

6. Answer: It was so hot outside, we had to sit in the shade.

Explanation: Students should be able to accurately reduce sentences by removing unnecessary words/phrases. The phrase "since it was hot" is not necessary because this is already stated in the sentence.

7. Answer: A

Explanation: The words *fussy* and *gently* would best expand the sentence based on context clues.

8. Answer: C

Explanation: The words *fierce* and *fragile* would best expand the sentence based on context clues.

9. Answer: B

Explanation: The words *carefully* and *wobbly* would best expand the sentence based on context clues.

10. Answer: D

Explanation: All of these words/phrases could expand the sentence.

11. Answer: A

Explanation: Poem 1 is written in an older English dialect, while the language in poem 2 is more modern.

12. Answer: C

Explanation: Both poems are written from the first person point-of-view.

13. Answer: B

Explanation: The line "With me 'twere always day" is the best example of English slang. Slang is an informal type of language. The word *'twere* is a slang form of the phrase "it were" or "it was."

14. Answer: D

Explanation: This line most likely means *which I can never enjoy* in modern English.

15. Answer: A

Explanation: Passage 1 is written in a slang dialect.

16. Answer: C

Explanation: Passage 2 is written in formal English.

17. Answer: C

Explanation: The dialogue in passage 1 is written in a casual, relaxed register. Register is the style of language used in different settings or conversation types. Ex.: The language used when chatting with a friend vs. giving a formal speech in class.

18. Answer: A

Explanation: The English style used in Passage 2 is more formal than Passage 1.

19. Answer: Answers will vary.

Explanation: Students should demonstrate an understanding of the difference between formal and informal English. Ex.: My father and I went hiking up the old, muddy mountain.

20. Answer: Answers will vary.

Explanation: Students should demonstrate an understanding of the difference between modern English and earlier forms of the language. Ex.: How does the eagle soar so high in the sky?

5. LANGUAGE

 prepaze

ANSWER KEY

5.3. Vocabulary Acquisition and Use

1. Answer: B

Explanation: The phrase "a deal" means a large amount or by a lot.

2. Answer: C

Explanation: In this context, the phrase "in spite of" means that the King family's attitude was not affected by their money.

3. Answer: B

Explanation: The word figure is referring to the shape of the sister Jo in the context of this text.

4. Answer: D

Explanation: Antonyms are words that have opposite meanings. The word *admire* is an antonym of the word *detest*.

5. Answer: B

Explanation: Synonyms are words that have similar meanings. The word *unusual* is a synonym of the word *remarkable.*

6. Answer: D

Explanation: This phrase most like means that Alice was eager to learn more.

7. Answer: B

Explanation: The word *suddenly* means *unexpectedly.*

8. Answer: C

Explanation: A synonym for the word *delight* is *pleasure.*

9. Answer: D

Explanation: The word *passage* most likely mean *a corridor* in the context of the text.

10. Answer: A

Explanation: The word *longed* means *had a strong wish or desire (wanted).*

11. Answer: Antonym

Explanation: The underlined word is an antonym of the word dishonesty.

12. Answer: Synonym

Explanation: The underlined word is a synonym of the word regret.

13. Answer: Affix

Explanation: The underlined affix means "wrong."

14. Answer: A

Explanation: The affix multi- means "many." The word lingual means "pertaining to language."

15. Answer: C

Explanation: The affix super- means "beyond"

16. Answer: C

Explanation: Homographs are words that are spelled the same, but can have different pronunciations and/or meanings. The word *compress* is a homograph.

17. Answer: D

Explanation: An idiom is a figure of speech that uses words in ways other than the literal meaning. The phrase "under the weather" is an idiom that means ill.

18. Answer: B

Explanation: This phrase means to go around the truth, so the sentence means he directly told the truth.

19. Answer: A

Explanation: This statement is true. A word beginning with the affix inter- most refers to something happening between two or more subjects.

20. Answer: A

Explanation: This statement is true. A glossary can be used to find the pronunciation of a word.

5. LANGUAGE

ANSWER KEY

5.4. Practice Test

1. Answer: B
Explanation: This statement is false. A homograph is a word that has more than one meaning.

2. Answer: B
Explanation: This statement is false. A metaphor is a figure of speech that is used to make a comparison between two things that are not actually alike.

3. Answer: C
Explanation: The word *and* is a conjunction used to connect the words *black* and *white*.

4. Answer: C
Explanation: Synonyms are words that have similar meanings. The word *regress* is not a synonym of the word *progress*.

5. Answer: A
Explanation: The word *progress* does not mean "a decline in development."

6. Answer: B
Explanation: The word progress is not used in a sentence on this dictionary page.

7. Answer: D
Explanation: The word homograph is best described as a homograph. Homographs are words that are spelled the same, but can have different pronunciations and/or meanings.

8. Answer: A
Explanation: We will be moving to Pennsylvania next summer. The verb phrase *will be moving* is in the future progressive tense and agrees with the action that occur next year.

9. Answer: A
Explanation: A book title should be underlined in a written essay. In a typed essay, a book title should be italicized.

10. Answer: Lisa, Janet, Brenda, and Molly were all invited to my sleepover.
Explanation: Students should be able to accurately use punctuation to separate list items in a sentence. This sentence requires commas.

11. Answer: For example, alligators have wider snouts than crocodiles.
Explanation: Students should be able to accurately separate introductory words/phrases from the rest of the sentence.

12. Answer: Mr. Brown is an archaeologist at the local museum.
Explanation: The words *archaeologist* and *museum* are misspelled in this sentence.

13. Answer: We attempted to locate the destination, but we were unsuccessful.
Explanation: The words *attempted, destination* and *unsuccessful* are misspelled in this sentence.

14. Answer: C
Explanation: The following is the best way to correct the shift in verb tense: She had been jogging for several miles before she finally reached her destination.

15. Answer: C
Explanation: The following is the best way to correct the shift in verb tense: He will have written 5 articles by the end of this year.

16. Answer: A
Explanation: The word *at* is a preposition used to indicate what time the movie started.

17. Answer: A
Explanation: The following is the best way to correct the shift in verb tense: I have been reading this magazine for the past fifteen minutes.

5. LANGUAGE

ANSWER KEY

18. Answer: B

Explanation: I have traveled to both Costa Rica and Mexico.

19. Answer: A

Explanation: We will still go camping whether it rains or not.

20. Answer: D

Explanation: All of these correlative conjunctions could complete the sentence.

21. Answer: Answers will vary.

Explanation: Students should be able to recognize and explain the literal meanings of figurative language. The phrase "an arm and a leg" means "very expensive."

22. Answer: Answers will vary.

Explanation: Students should be able to recognize and explain the literal meanings of figurative language. The phrase "courageous as a lion" means "very brave."

23. Answer: The nighttime sky looks amazing, doesn't it?

Explanation: Students should be able to accurately set off words/phrases from the rest of the sentence. The phrase *isn't it* is a tag question and should be set off with a comma.

24. Answer: Melissa, I am extremely disappointed in you.

Explanation: Students should be able to accurately set off words/phrases from the rest of the sentence. The name *Melissa* indicates a direct address in this sentence and should be set off with a comma.

25. Answer: Answers will vary.

Explanation: Students should be able to recognize and explain the literal meanings of figurative language. The phrase "music to my ears" means "pleasant to hear."

26. Answer: Answers will vary.

Explanation: Students should be able to recognize and explain the literal meanings of figurative language. The phrase "raindrops knocked" means that the rain made a loud noise on the window.

27. Answer: D

Explanation: TV show, book, and play titles should all be italicized.

28. Answer: B

Explanation: This statement is false. A thesaurus can be used to find antonyms of a word.

29. Answer: A

Explanation: A word with the affix sub- most likely refers to something underneath or below.

30. Answer: C

Explanation: The word *prompt* is misspelled as *promp*.

END OF YEAR ASSESSMENT

1. Answer: B

Explanation: The word experts most likely means specialists in the context of this text.

2. Answer: Answers may vary.

Explanation: Students should be able to write a paragraph about the problem/solution text structure. The paragraph should also be written in the first person, or from the student's point of view.

3. Answer: Answers may vary.

Explanation: Students should be able to explain how two texts written about the same topic can differ in structure, point-of-view etc.

4. Answer: A

Explanation: A search engine can be used to look up information by entering keywords or phrases.

prep⊙ze   **www.prepaze.com**

ANSWER KEY

5. Answer: A
Explanation: "Read Books, Not Tablets" is an appropriate tile for an opinion piece. This title expresses the author's position.

6. Answer: A
Explanation: This statement is true. You could use a dictionary and a history website to write a research paper about word origins.

7. Answer: A
Explanation: This statement is true. You could use a novel to write an opinion piece about its author.

8. Answer: B
Explanation: The word so is a conjunction used to connect two clauses.

9. Answer: C
Explanation: Article titles should appear in quotation marks.

10. Answer: D
Explanation: All of these strategies are helpful when looking for unknown word meanings.

11. Answer: B
Explanation: The word *timid* is best defined as lacking courage or shy.

12. Answer: A
Explanation: A thesaurus is used to find words with similar meanings. The words shrank, diminished, and ebbed best describe the word *dwindled*.

13. Answer: B
Explanation: The poem describes a day on April 18, 1775.

14. Answer: A
Explanation: This line from the poem is referring to a battle between the country-folk and the British troops.

15. Answer: B
Explanation: The theme of the poem is not self-discovery; it is a theme of war/battle.

16. Answer: B
Explanation: The narrator of the poem is speaking to children.

17. Answer: B
Explanation: The main event of the poem is describing two friends preparing to give a warning to the country-folk about the British troops attacking.

18. Answer: A
Explanation: Lanterns are used as a warning signal in the poem: "one if by land, two if by sea."

19. Answer: A
Explanation: A main idea of the text is that tornado scientists use instruments like the tornado probe to warn others about dangerous tornados approaching.

20. Answer: B
Explanation: A tornado probe is orange and cone-shaped.

21. Answer: A
Explanation: Scientists use tornado probes to predict future tornados.

22. Answer: B
Explanation: The text does not give a name to the tornado scientists.

23. Answer: B
Explanation: The text is not about the massive destruction of tornados.

24. Answer: A
Explanation: The line does add support to why tornado probes are important tools.

25. Answer: C
Explanation: The King would have to explain how people know who is the king in order for the rest of the story to take place.

ANSWER KEY

26. Answer: D
Explanation: The boy is unsure whether the king is really the king.

27. Answer: D
Explanation: Briskly means quickly and cantered refers to the way the horse was moving.

28. Answer: The King offered the boy a ride to see the king and even revealed who he was.
Explanation: Only a compassionate king would have done that for a boy.

29. Answer: A
Explanation: The problem is only beginning as a conflict so this is setting the scene for what is about to take place later.

30. Answer: D
Explanation: The mice are too scared to do the plan that they came up with.

31. Answer: A
Explanation: In a video, viewers would experience the sounds just as Timmy Willie did.

32. Answer: A
Explanation: The reader can learn various information about kites.

33. Answer: C
Explanation: An article about kite flying techniques would best help to develop the topic.

34. Answer: B
Explanation: A dictionary definition of the word kite would not be relevant to the topic.

35. Answer: D
Explanation: All of these statements are true.

36. Answer: A
Explanation: If sugary items are taxed, people will have to pay more. If they have to pay more, hopefully, they will choose healthier options.

37. Answer: A
Explanation: Informational writing should be free from opinions.

38. Answer: D
Explanation: All of the listed words are vocabulary words specific to outer space.

39. Answer: Answers will vary.
Explanation: Students should be able to produce writing that is appropriate to task, purpose, and audience.

40. Answer: B
Explanation: A fairytale is most likely not based on facts, and would not be a reliable resource for this type of research.

41. Answer: A
Explanation: An article written by a doctor would be the best resource for researching this topic.

42. Answer: D
Explanation: The webpage might be a good resource for researching all of these topics.

43. Answer: B
Explanation: This webpage would not be helpful for researching how bones break and mend.

44. Answer: B
Explanation: The word stationery most likely means notepaper in the context of this text.

45. Answer: A
Explanation: The theme of both passages is life and death.

REFERENCES CITED

- *A Boy and His Stomach,* from Poems Teachers Ask For

- An Excerpt from *The Tale of Johnny Town-Mouse*

- *Civil Rights on a City Bus* By ReadWorks

- Excerpt adapted from the article *"What Should Students Have for Lunch?"* By McClatchy-Tribune News Service

- Excerpt from *"A Fable" from Poems Teachers Ask For* By Ralph Waldo Emerson

- Excerpt from *"A Song for Harlem: 1928"* By Patricia McKissack

- Excerpt from *"Abby Takes a Stand: 1960"* By Patricia McKissack

- Excerpt from *"How to Teach Microsoft Word to Kids"* By Joana Polisena

- Excerpt from *"The Blind Boy",* By Colley Cibber

- Excerpt from *"Triceratops Dinosaur"s,* By Ken Nelson

- Excerpt from *"When I Was a Boy"* By Eugene Field

- Excerpt from *Alice's Adventures in Wonderland,* By Lewis Carroll

- Excerpt from *Elijah of Buxton,* By Christopher Paul Curtis

- Excerpt from *Gods and Heroes,* By R. E. Francillon

- Excerpt from *Holes,* By Louis Sachar

- Excerpt from *In the Days of Giants,* By Abbie Farwell Brown

- Excerpt from the article *"A Brief Summary of the Interesting Life Cycle of a Chicken"* By Animal Sake

- Excerpt from the article *"African-American Civil Rights Movement"* By Ken Nelson

- Excerpt from the article *"Brown Bears",* By National Geographic Kids

- Excerpt from the article "Classification of Bodies of Water", By Jamie Witt

REFERENCES CITED

- Excerpt from the article *"Countries of The World: Honduras"*, By National Geographic Kids

- Excerpt from the article *"Culture & History"*, By EnjoyHonduras

- Excerpt from the article *"How Does Fluoride Work?"*, By KidsHealth

- Excerpt from the article *"In their Own Corner of the Antarctic, these Penguins are Living Life"*, By Damian Carrington

- Excerpt from the article *"More Schools are Allowing Phones, So Teachers Use Them for Education"*, By Associated Press

- Excerpt from the article *"Sneaky Marketing: School Reward Programs Push Junk Food, Experts Say"*, By The Washington Post

- Excerpt from *The Dentist and the Crocodile*, By Roald Dahl

- Excerpt from *The Giver*, By Lois Lowry

- Excerpt from *Long Walk to Freedom*, The Autobiography of Nelson Mandela

- *Fifty Famous People*, By James Baldwin

- *Full of Life*, By Walt Whitman

- *GPS*, By ReadWorks

- *Grimms' Fairy Tales*, By The Brothers Grimm

- *Honeybees*, By ReadWorks

- *Life*, By Charlotte Bronte

- *Paul Revere's Ride*, By Henry Wadsworth Longfellow

- *Peter Cottontail*, Written by Thomas Burgess

- *Shining a New Light on Growing Food Indoors*, By Washington Post

- *The Animals' Plea*, By Rosi Caswell

- *The Little Old Woman Who Lived in a Shoe*, By Joseph Martin Kronheim

www.prepaze.com